3804

Story of the Year

☆

the
ten winning
Stories

INDEPENDENT

Story of the Year

☆

the ten winning Stories

Rachel Adams, Lynne Benton,
Jennifer Gleason, Eleanor Lang,
Richard Nathanson, Richard Newton,
Finbar O'Connor, Ghillian Potts,
Brenda Sivers, Jonathan Wakeham.

The Federation of Children's Book Groups

■SCHOLASTIC

Scholastic Children's Books,
Commonwealth House, 1–19 New Oxford Street,
London WC1A 1NU, UK
a division of Scholastic Ltd
London ~ New York ~ Toronto ~ Sydney ~ Auckland

Published in the UK by Scholastic Ltd, 1996

ISBN 0 590 54269 9

Typeset by DP Photosetting, Aylesbury, Bucks.
Printed in the UK by Clays Ltd, St Ives plc

10 9 8 7 6 5 4 3 2 1

Contents

Introduction

Welcome, for the fourth year running, to the Story of the Year! Here are 1996's ten best children's stories for six to nine-year-olds, winners of the *Independent*/Scholastic Story of the Year Competition.

Once again, we were overwhelmed with a fantastic array of stories to choose from. Over two and a half thousand people sent theirs in – which were then, with much agonizing, shortlisted to twenty-one. Then the judges stepped in – Wendy Berliner, *Independent* education editor; Adrian Edmonson, actor and writer; David Fickling, Publishing Director of Scholastic Children's Books; Blake Morrison, author and journalist; Michael Watts, editor of the *Independent* magazine; and José Williams, deputy chair of the Federation of Children's Book Groups – an organization to promote interest and enjoyment in children's books and reading. She represented the children in the voting – pupils from four schools read the shortlisted stories and their votes were instrumental in the final outcome. Every one of these people – judges and children – had their own favourite, and each fought hard and persuasively for them! But after much soul-searching and discussion the final ten stories were chosen.

And what a brilliant and varied collection they chose! The winner was unanimous – the lyrical and resonant story *The Sheltie*, set in Orkney by Eleanor Lang, who was born there. And then the two runners-up; the hilarious fairy tale *Spellshocked*, by Irish author Finbar O'Connor (also a winner two years ago!); and the lovely, reassuring *A Present for Gran* by Lynne Benton. But *all* the stories in this luminous collection are winners in their own, sometimes very different ways.

Anyway, see for yourself. Do you agree with this year's choices? Which is *your* favourite?

Happy reading!

Scholastic Children's Books

Winner

The Sheltie

ELEANOR LANG

Illustrated by
IAN BECK

*To Mark, Deborah, William and Donna –
my best critics.*

Once, there was a fine young couple lived on a croft in Orkney. There were four strapping young boys, and some years later, a daughter, born to the farmer and his wife. This girl never grew as big and brosy as her brothers, but remained slight and short for her age, although she had enough fire and determination to make up for it. She was christened Wilhelmina after her father, but she was called Minnie by everyone. She was always made much of by the family, as she was so much the youngest and the smallest of the children.

They were something terrible poor. One by one, the boys were obliged to leave home and seek work on another farm, or in a distant town. They all vowed to keep in touch, and come home once every year at Christmas time. Soon, only

Minnie was left at home with her parents. That year, the summer was very bad. The rain fell from the sky in sheets, and ruined the crop which was waiting to be harvested. The corn lay and mouldered on the ground. When the farmer and his wife gathered together what provisions they had, it was obvious that it would hardly feed *them*, never mind their daughter.

"Don't worry," said Minnie, seeing the problem immediately. "I'll go and work for the old Spey-Wife over the hills. I hear she's been looking for a servant."

Minnie's mother had dreaded this moment.

"Is there no other place would take ye on, lass? I've heard tell the old Spey-Wife works spells and wickedness on folk."

"Never a bit of it, Mother, I'll be just fine," said Minnie, and she went straight away to gather her few belongings into a bundle.

Nevertheless, it was with dragging feet and a heavy heart that she set out for the house of the Witch. For as long as she was in sight of her own home, her steps were jaunty and she hummed to herself; but once the croft had faded into the horizon, her song faltered. She stopped once to

eat from the food which her mother had pre-
pared for her. By the time she was on the road
which led to the Spey-Wife's dwelling, up among
the stone quarries of the high peat-bogs and hills,
dusk had started to dim the sky.

The old Witch watched her all the way up the
hill.

With uncertain steps, and many a look cast
about her, Minnie went up to the lichen-covered
door. She raised her hand to knock, but the door
flew open before she could touch it.

"Come away in, lass, come away in. I've been
expectin' ye," said a wavering voice from the
gloom of the interior.

"Sit doon, and we'll discuss terms," ordered
the voice.

A black shadow moved between Minnie and
the far wall, and threw a peat on the fire. By the
light of the shower of blue and gold sparks which
flew up, Minnie was able to make out a simple
wooden table with a chair beside it. The Spey-
Wife settled into a straw-backed chair by the
fireside, and Minnie nervously sat on the seat by
the table. For a few minutes, there was no sound
but the hissing of the fire and the mournful

"swee" from a battered kettle which was sus-
pended over it.

Finally the Witch spoke.

"The question is, do you see, are you the right
person for the job? Are you able for it?"

"I can carry water, and cook and clean. I'm
small but I'm strong," said Minnie. "What
would you pay me?" she added boldly.

"I'll pay you with a roof over your head, and
food on the table, girl," said the Witch. "How
will you pay *me* for all the knowledge I will give
you, and all the spells and secrets you will
learn?"

"I have nothing," said Minnie, suddenly
crestfallen, "but these few things in my bundle,
and they're no' worth a pin, but to me."

"My, but you have bonnie hair, lass," said the
Witch.

With a shock, Minnie realized that the old
woman had moved up behind her in the gloom,
because she could feel her bony fingers stroking
and caressing her hair.

"I could use that hair to make some fine love
potions," crooned the Witch, "if there was a bit
more of it. I'll tell you what, lass," she went on.

"You will work for me, and learn all the wisdom I have, and I will see that you are fed and clothed, until such time as your hair has grown to your waist, and then you will cut it off, and give it to me to make spells, and you will be free to go. That is as fair a bargain as I can offer. What do you say?"

Minnie agreed to the terms. "But I would like to visit home once a year, on Christmas Day," she said.

"I'm no' just too sure if that's the best o' ideas," murmured the Witch, as she went to attend to the fire, for if truth be told, the old woman was as hard as "get-out".

So Minnie started her isolated but busy life, working in the home of the Spey-Wife. Apart from her domestic duties, the Witch taught her which herbs and berries to pick for spell-casting. Once she had learned these secrets, Minnie was able to go collecting on the moors by herself, and her only happy moments were spent there.

On a day of wild wind, she would jump between tussocks of heather, as she watched white horses' manes breaking in the navy waters of the distant sea.

On sunny days she would take off her heavy leather boots, and paddle in the peaty waters of the hill-puddles, at first repelled, but then delighted with the spongy feel of the velvety mosses squelching under her toes.

On a mild day of smirry rain, she would go out without her cloak, and exult in the feel of rainwater running down her long hair, and the damp swish of soft grasses brushing against her bare knees. Then she would go back to the house, and steam dry at the peat-fire.

Dead things were peculiarly effective to spellmaking. Minnie was instructed to bring home as many drowned dragonflies, as many insects halfdigested in sundew-leaves as she could find. Once she came across an old cat which had crept away to the moors to die. When she first saw it, it was furry-coated and might have just been sleeping, but when she turned it over gingerly with her toe, she saw that its head and body on the underside had been eaten to the bone by worms. The Witch was pleased and excited with this find, and made many powerful spells with the bones.

People often visited the house, to ask for potions to take away, and enchantments to be cast. Minnie was always told to hide out of sight during these visits, in case she guessed the identity of the callers, many of whom were rich and powerful people.

As the days wore on, Minnie longed for Christmas Day to come, so that she might feel the love and comfort of her own home again, if only for one day, but the Spey-Wife had other plans. She had no intention of letting anyone with so much knowledge of her secrets out of her sight.

On Christmas Eve, she mixed a sleeping-draught for Minnie, and gave it to her to drink, pretending it was a Christmas treat. The magic in the potion kept Minnie asleep for the whole day and when she awoke the next morning, she had lost track of time, and thought that Christmas was still to come.

At the same time, the Witch sent word to Minnie's family that their daughter had unfortunately lost her way in the hills, and had fallen into a flooded quarry and drowned.

The family were heartbroken. As the Witch had assured them that no body would ever be found, they fashioned a little wooden cross and set it in the garden, in memory of their bright, bonnie wee girl.

So, by way of wicked enchantments, the Witch kept Minnie under her evil spell, until five years passed, and Minnie's hair had grown to her waist. She went to ask the Witch if the bargain could now be paid off. But the old Spey-Wife, who was as cold as love on a Monday morning, had no intention of letting her servant go.

"What kind of payment is this you are offering for the knowledge I have shared with you? Two handspans of straggly black hair? Go back to your duties, girl. Ask me again, when your hair has grown to your knees!"

So, poor Minnie went back to her chores.

There was one secret that the Witch had not shared with her, and it was this: as she watched the young woman at work, the Witch envied Minnie her youth and vitality, her keen eyes and light step. She had determined to work on a transformation spell, so that she could exchange her own worn-out body for Minnie's younger one. But it would require very powerful magic, and she had not so far been able to work out a formula.

Minnie toiled on for several more years, by

which time her hair had grown down to her knees.

Once more, she confronted the old Spey-Wife.

"Well then, lass, I see your hair is grown to your knees," said the Witch, circling Minnie, and feeding the long tresses through her hands. "But what is this I see? Is that no' some grey hairs hidin' among the black? Fie on you, girl, for grey hairs are no' worth a button tae me for spells. I fear you'll have to bide wi' me a while yet!"

When she heard this, Minnie's eyes were opened. She saw into the old Witch's heart, and it was as black as the Earl o' Hell's waistcoat. She realized that the Witch had never had any intention of letting her go.

Snatching up the transformation spell, which was sitting half-made in a bottle on the table, she fled out of the open door, determined to make a bid for freedom.

The old woman fairly screeched with rage, as she hirpled after the runaway.

Minnie turned and flung the spell-bottle as hard as she could at her pursuer, but the Spey-Wife managed to dodge it and retrieve it un-damaged. She took out the stopper, and flung the unfinished spell over Minnie.

Minnie was straight away transformed; but into a fine black pony, with a strong back, and stuggy legs, and a bonnie black-and-grey flecked mane and tail.

When she saw that the spell had not worked as she had hoped, and all her plans had come to nothing, the Spey-Wife's wicked heart burst with rage. Her evil form slithered and trickled away down into the ground, where it poisoned the well-water for the next ten years.

As for the black pony, she tossed her head and galloped off for home. How she flicked her heels, and snickered in delight, when she caught sight of her old dwelling! Much had changed there during her long absence. The eldest son had done well, and returned home with a good fortune. Now the house was well furnished, and had plenty of food in the presses and larders. The three other boys had married, and lived close by with their wives and children.

The eldest brother was in the garden repairing a dyke when Minnie trotted up to him. She jumped over the wall, walked to the memorial cross, and gently dislodged it with her hoof.

Then she returned to her brother and nuzzled his collar, while he petted and spoke to her.

"Mother! Father! Come here!" he shouted. "You'll maybe think I've gone stone mad, but this peedie horse fair has the look o' our Minnie!"

So the little horse was made a great fuss of, and became a family pet who was much loved by all, and gave rides to the children and grandchildren.

And to this day in Orkney, you will see short, sturdy little horses, who love to roam over the hillsides. Their correct name is Shetland ponies, but the Islanders call them Shelties. They have independent spirits, however, so do not be over-familiar with them, or try to run your fingers through their manes. They may well object, and take a snap at your hands, if you are not careful.

ELEANOR LANG

Eleanor Lang was born on the Orkney Islands. She studied in classical and modern ballet, mime and drama in Glasgow, and has mostly lived there since, working as a dancer, and then as a book keeper and proof-reader. She is married to Michael and they have four children; two boys and two girls. She enjoys writing (her story "The Lunch-box Imp" was a runner-up for the Academy of Children's writers story competition in 1994) and painting (her paintings have been exhibited at Glasgow School of Art and are sold locally). Happiness for her is a book store, or a gallery. Double happiness is an art exhibition with one of her pictures in it, or a book store with one of her stories in it!

She says: "I started writing stories to amuse my younger daughter (now eleven) about three years ago. I am not keen on the American cartoon hero, who zaps people with super-powers. The only secret weapon any of us possess is our own courage. I am intrigued by the longevity of traditional fairy tales, and I like old-fashioned values.

"I tried to write 'The Sheltie' using the sayings and speech rhythms of my Orcadian grandmother."

Runner-up

Spellshocked

FINBAR O'CONNOR

Illustrated by
JAN LEWIS

To my nephews Simon, Aidan and Jeremy Ostinelli, and Liam Levey.

T he Queen was having a baby and outside the royal bedroom the Royal Librarian, the Court Astrologer and the editor of the *Daily Dragon* were waiting eagerly for news.

Suddenly the bedroom door flew open and the King rushed out in his nightshirt with his crown perched crookedly on his head.

"It's a boy!" he cried joyfully, doing somersaults around the hallway.

"An heir to the throne!" said the Royal Librarian happily.

"Just as I predicted!" said the Court Astrologer smugly.

"THE BOY WHO WILL BE KING!" scribbled the editor of the *Daily Dragon*. "Our readers will love this!"

"I mean to say," cried the King, dancing on the furniture, "it's a *girl!*"

"An heir*ess* to the throne!" said the Royal Librarian hastily.

"It was all in the stars," said the Court Astrologer complacently.

"THE QUEEN OF OUR HEARTS!" scribbled the editor of the *Daily Dragon*. "Our readers will love this!"

"That is, it's neither, or rather it's both!" cried the King, turning cartwheels down the stairs.

"Are you feeling quite all right, sire?" asked the Royal Librarian anxiously.

"I saw this coming, of course," said the Court Astrologer knowingly.

"KING GOES BONKERS!" scribbled the editor of the *Daily Dragon*. "Our readers will *really* love this!"

"It's twins, you idiots," said the King, flopping down on a sofa and mopping his brow. "A boy *and* a girl!"

"Congratulations, sire!" said the Royal Librarian.

"I *said* it would be one or the other," said the Court Astrologer. "I'm never wrong, you know."

"ROYAL MIXED DOUBLES!" scribbled the editor of the *Daily Dragon*. "Oh well, I suppose it'll have to do!"

The King and Queen were delighted with their new babies. Every morning, while the Queen was doing her post-natal exercises, the King rushed down to the nursery to change their nappies before breakfast while the Royal Nanny (who had looked after the King when *he* was a baby) stood by, wringing her hands anxiously and saying, "*Please* be careful, sire!"

"Oh, stop fussing, woman," said the King, as he balanced a baby on each knee and busily powdered their bottoms. "I *am* their father, after all!"

"Your royal father never powdered *your* bottom, your majesty," said Nanny crossly. "That was always *my* job!"

"Leave my bottom out of this, Nanny," snapped the King. "And stop being so old-fashioned. This *is* the Middle Ages, you know!"

One morning when the twins were six weeks old and the King was in the nursery as usual, the Queen came in, looking worried.

"Oh, Kingy-Poo?" said the Queen.

"Yes, Queeny-Pie?" replied the King, not taking his eyes off the twins who were lying in their cot, kicking their legs and gurgling.

"I'm afraid there's trouble in the Kingdom, darling," said the Queen.

"That's nice, precious," replied the King. "Say *Da-Da*, baby. *Da-Da?*"

"A mean old dragon has been devouring people in the Eastern Forest," said the Queen.

"Splendid, splendid!" said the King. "Say *Ma-Ma*, baby. *Ma-Ma?*"

"And a great big giant has been squashing people in the Western Wood," said the Queen.

"Marvellous, wonderful!" said the King. "Which of 'em looks more like me, d'you think?"

The Queen was puzzled for a moment, but then she realized he was talking about the babies.

"Anyway," said the Queen, "I thought I'd just ride out with the knights and slay something, don't you know?"

"Excellent idea, dearest," said the King, who hadn't heard a word. "Have a lovely time!"

So the Queen (who, of course, loved her babies

but got bored hanging around the castle all day) galloped off to take care of things in the Kingdom while the King (who, of course, loved his subjects but got bored galloping around slaying things all day) stayed at home and took care of things in the nursery.

Everything went on happily until the twins were a year old and the arrangements for their first birthday party got under way. The King was in a good mood because the Court Astrologer had confidently predicted that the weather would be fine (as long as it didn't rain), and the Queen was in a good mood because she loved organizing things.

"I'm sure our readers would like to know who will be at the party," said the editor of the *Daily Dragon* (who was hoping for an invitation).

"Oh, just family," said the King. "Relations, close friends, that sort of thing."

"Say about five hundred in all," added the Queen.

"And birthday cake for all our subjects, of course," chortled the King.

"LET THEM EAT CAKE SAYS KING!" scribbled the editor. "Very generous of you, sire!"

Just then, the Royal Librarian came in.

"Sire," he said, "I have been reading books in the Royal Library."

"Well, that's nothing to be ashamed of, man," said the King jovially. "I read a book myself once!"

"But sire," said the Royal Librarian, "according to these books it is absolutely imperative that you invite a witch to their Highnesses' birthday party!"

"Invite a witch to my children's party?" spluttered the King. "Have you taken leave of your senses, Librarian?"

"But all the best authorities recommend it, your majesty," said the Royal Librarian.

"What authorities are these?" asked the King.

"Well, sire," stammered the Royal Librarian, "there's *My First Book of Fairy Tales* and *Nursery Tales For Tiny Tots* and—"

"Now listen here, Librarian," interrupted the King. "As I keep telling Nanny this isn't Once-Upon-A-Time any more. We're a modern, progressive kingdom, we are! Why, only last Wednesday we discovered the... What do you call that thing that goes round and round? They put 'em on carts and such."

"The wheel, sire?" said the Royal Librarian.

"The wheel, exactly," said the King. "Marvellous invention. Saves a lot of wear and tear on peasants ... anyway, the point is it's time to forget these old superstitions. So, no witches at my children's party, and no giants, wizards or dragons either, eh what?"

"If you say so, sire," said the Royal Librarian.

"I do say so, sire!" said the King firmly. "You read too many books, Librarian, that's your trouble! Just forget about books and get on with running the library!"

"Yes, sire," said the Royal Librarian with a sigh.

The day of the party dawned bright and sunny. ("I told you so!" said the Royal Astrologer.) Two long tables were set out in the castle gardens with the King at the head of one and the Queen at the head of the other. The twins sat in highchairs under the blossoming trees and gurgled and cooed and were admired by everybody. The guests ate and drank and sang and laughed while the editor of the *Daily Dragon* prowled around eavesdropping on conversations and making notes for his gossip column. The only person who looked unhappy was the Royal Librarian. Suddenly dark clouds blotted out the sun, lightning flashed and there was an ominous roll of thunder. ("Just as I foretold!" said the Royal Astrologer.)

Then a great black raven came flapping across the garden and perched on a branch above the babies' heads. The blossoms withered and fell from the tree as the raven spread its shadowy wings and opened its sword-sharp bill and croaked in a harsh voice:

"SLEEP LIKE DEATH THE OLD KING'S
  DAUGHTER
OLD KING'S SON SHALL DWELL IN
  WATER
FOREVER THIS SPELL LASTS
  UNLESS—"

But even as the raven spoke the King sprang from his seat, snatched a bow from one of the

guards, took careful aim and shot an arrow at the bird's black breast.

"No, sire!" cried the Royal Librarian. But he was too late. The raven screeched as the arrow pierced its heart and fell dead on the ground, scorching the grass where it lay.

("CRACK SHOT KING GETS A BIRDIE!" scribbled the editor of the *Daily Dragon.)*

Black vapour engulfed the raven's body and when it had cleared the bird had vanished and an old witch with a sword-sharp face and a cloak of black feathers lay dead on the ground.

("CALLOUS KING SHOOTS PENSIONER!" scribbled the editor of the *Daily Dragon.*)

"My babies!" cried the Queen in horror, for the Princess lay pale in a sleep like death and where the young Prince had been sitting a hideous green frog squatted and croaked.

"I *knew* this would happen!" sighed the Royal Librarian.

"That's just what *I* was going to say!" said the Court Astrologer.

The King and Queen sat in the throne room and wept.

"I tried to warn you, sire," said the Royal Librarian. "Witches get terribly offended if you don't invite them to birthday parties. They can be very spiteful about things like that."

"I should have listened to you from the start, Librarian," said the King. "You're the only one around here who talks any sense!" (The Court Astrologer looked insulted but said nothing.)

"Sire," said the Librarian, "you did right to kill the witch. But she died before she had finished her spell. If you had waited until the spell was finished it would have told us how to break the enchantment."

"Then what can we do?" asked the King. "Are my children to remain cursed for ever?"

"I must study the books in the Royal Library," said the Librarian. "Somewhere in those books I am sure to find the answer. But it may take many years."

"Begin at once then," said the King. "We have no time to lose!"

And so the Princess was laid in a bed in a high tower and a young soldier was set by her side to guard her. The Prince was placed in a pond in the castle garden where a young kitchen-maid was sent to look after him. As for the Librarian, he shut himself in the library and began to study the books, searching for the spell that would release the royal twins from their enchantment.

Long years passed. The young soldier sat in the tower and sang songs to the sleeping Princess and she heard him in her dreams and smiled as she slept. The little kitchen-maid brought food to the Frog-Prince and stroked his knobbly head with stalks of grass while he sat in her hand and blinked at her. And as the Princess grew older she grew more beautiful so that the young soldier fell in love with her. And though the Prince did not grow handsomer as he grew older the kitchen-maid got used to his ugliness so that she grew to love him also.

Finally, one day when fifteen years had passed, the Librarian entered the throne room where the King and Queen were sitting. His back was bent from long years of poring over books and his eyes were weak and watery from long nights of reading by candlelight. But on his face he wore a tired smile.

"Sire," he said, "I have found the answer!"

"Where?" asked the King in amazement.

"In here," said the Librarian, holding up a book.

"*The Frog Prince, the Sleeping Beauty and Other Favourite Tales*," read the King. "And this book has the answer?"

"Yes, sire," said the Librarian, and opening the book he read in a loud voice:

"SLEEP LIKE DEATH THE OLD KING'S
   DAUGHTER
OLD KING'S SON SHALL DWELL IN
   WATER
FOREVER THIS SPELL LASTS UNLESS
THEY'RE KISSED BY PRINCE AND BY
   PRINCESS."

"I could have told you that!" said the Court Astrologer.

"KISS AND WAKE UP!" scribbled the editor of the *Daily Dragon*.

"Summon every prince and princess in the land," cried the King joyfully. "Tell them that the ones who break this spell shall be married to my son and daughter!"

*   *   *

A few days later, the King and Queen sat in the throne room looking at the great crowd of princes and princesses who had gathered there, hoping to be the ones to break the spell and marry into the Royal Family.

"Just look at the state of them!" said the King gloomily. "Ridiculous powdered wigs, faces covered in make-up, and as for those *hideous* tights!"

"Yes, dear," said the Queen. "And the princesses are even worse!"

A sudden silence fell as the doors opened and the young soldier strode into the hall carrying the sleeping Princess in his arms. Behind him came the little kitchen-maid with the Frog-Prince squatting and blinking in her hand.

"Gad, what a scrawny little gel!" drawled one of the princes. "I hope she doesn't have bedsores! Wot? Wot?"

"Does one really have to kiss that horrid frog?" brayed a princess. "One hopes it doesn't give one warts!"

The soldier and the kitchen-maid stood before the throne.

The kitchen-maid hung her head and a tear

trickled from her eye, but the soldier looked proudly at the King and spoke in a strong voice.

"Sire," he said, "we are but humble servants of your majesty. But for fifteen years we have watched over your children. And now we have a favour to ask."

"Ask it," said the King.

"Before we give them up to their royal destiny..." said the soldier.

"We should like to kiss them goodbye," said the little kitchen-maid in a terrified whisper.

"Egad, dashed impertinence!" drawled a prince. "I've a good mind to punch that fellow on the nose!"

"Commoners kissing royalty!" brayed a princess. "They'll be wanting to marry us next!"

"Silence!" thundered the King. Then he smiled at the soldier and the kitchen-maid. "Your favour is granted," he said.

"Well, really!" brayed a princess.

"It weminds one of the worst excesses of the Fwench Wevolution!" drawled a prince.

The soldier bent and kissed the sleeping Princess and a great gasp went up from the watching crowd. For as soon as his lips touched hers she blinked and woke and smiled at him.

"I thought you were only a dream," she said.

At the same time the kitchen-maid kissed the Frog-Prince.

This time there came an even louder gasp and several princesses screamed and fainted. For the frog had vanished and there, standing hand in hand with the kitchen-maid, was a handsome young prince, dripping wet and totally naked! The Librarian hastily covered him with a cloak. ("PRINCE DISPLAYS FAMILY JEWELS!" scribbled the editor of the *Daily Dragon*, wishing that photography had been invented.)

"Well, that's that," said the King, ignoring the outraged protests of the watching princes and princesses. "They broke the spell so they marry my son and daughter."

"But sire," said the Royal Librarian, "he's a soldier and she's a kitchen-maid. They are not of royal blood!"

"If this kitchen-maid marries my son she'll be a princess, yes?" said the King.

"Well, yes, sire," said the Librarian.

"And if this soldier marries my daughter he'll be a prince?" asked the King.

"Well, strictly speaking..." began the Librarian.

"I knew you'd agree with me," said the King. "So now it's all settled."

"I predict they will all live happily ever after!" said the Court Astrologer.

"That's what all the books say, anyway!" said the Royal Librarian.

"Well, I hope you're wrong," said the editor of the *Daily Dragon*.

"Why do you say that?" asked the King in astonishment.

"I'll tell you why I say it, sire," said the editor gloomily. "Because happy endings don't make headlines!"

FINBAR O'CONNOR

Finbar O'Connor was born in Dublin, and after graduating from Trinity College, Dublin, with a degree in French and English, he joined Dublin Public Libraries and has worked as a librarian for ten years. He is married to Margaret Levey, a barrister, and has just become a fully-qualified barrister-at-law himself, as she kept winning all the arguments! He has had many songs, poems, and stories published in Ireland, and is the first author to have won twice in the Story of the Year Competition! His story, "The Princess in the Tower Block" was one of the winners in Story of the Year 2.

He says: "I began writing children's poetry and songs for educational publishers and subsequently branched out into more general children's writing. I try to write stories that will entertain adults as well as children in order to avoid inducing terminal boredom in anybody unfortunate enough to have to read the same piece over and over again."

Runner - up

A Present
For Gran

LYNNE BENTON

Illustrated by
VALERIA PETRONE

For my ever-supportive husband, Robin, and our four talented and creative children, Claire, David, Tim and Louise, with love.

"**H**urry up, Danny, you'll be late for school!" called Mum.

Danny put down the spaceship he was making out of a bit of cardboard. He'd have to finish it after school.

He hoped it wasn't one of Mum's clearing-up days. If it was, she would probably throw it out. She never understood what Danny wanted to keep.

"You're so untidy, Danny!" she was always saying. "Just like your dad."

As he ran downstairs and grabbed his school bag, she said the other thing she was always saying.

"You always leave things till the last minute! Just like your dad!"

Dad had left them when Danny was little, and

now he was living in Australia with his new wife. He still sent cards for birthdays and Christmas, but Danny couldn't really remember him any more. And Mum only mentioned him when Danny did something she didn't like.

"You're just like your dad!" she said, with That Look on her face.

Jessica was not like Dad at all, at least, according to Mum. Jessica was perfect. Jessica was just like Mum.

It was hard having a sister who was perfect. She was five years older than Danny, and very clever. Mum was very proud of her.

Danny wished Mum would be proud of him sometimes, but he didn't seem to be good at the right things.

He was good at making models out of bits and pieces. But if Mum found them, she could never see what they were going to be; she thought they were rubbish and threw them away.

He wasn't much good at reading, or Maths, and his writing wasn't wonderful either. And those were the things Mum thought were important.

Jessica read books full of hard words, came

top in school exams, and won prizes.

It wasn't fair.

That afternoon, when he got home from school, his room was horribly tidy, and his model had disappeared.

"You've thrown my spaceship away!" said Danny.

"Well, how was I supposed to know you wanted to keep it?" said Mum. "There was so much rubbish in your room! You're so untidy, Danny. Just like your dad!"

Danny sighed. He'd heard it all before.

That evening Mum reminded them that it was Gran's birthday on Saturday, and they were going to see her for the day.

Gran was Dad's mother, and she lived a long way away, so they didn't see her very often. But she still wanted to see them, even after Dad had left.

Danny liked going to Gran's. Gran didn't scold him all the time for being untidy or late. And he could play with Rex.

Rex was Gran's dog. He was a red setter, Gran said, and although he was getting old now, he still enjoyed a game of ball.

"I'm going to buy Gran some bubble bath for her birthday," said Jessica.

"Good idea," said Mum. "I've got her a book. Now, what are *you* going to buy her, Danny? I hope you've got some money left."

Danny shuffled his feet. He'd forgotten about Gran's birthday, and he'd spent all his money. And if he asked for more, Mum would get cross and tell him he was hopeless with money, just like Dad. He didn't want to set her off again.

"I'm going to make her present," he said.

Jessica laughed.

"Gran won't want one of your silly models, Danny! You're not a baby any more. You've got to give her a proper present."

"I know that!" scowled Danny. "Of course it'll be a proper present."

Mum looked a bit worried, so he added, "You'll see!"

But later, in bed, he wondered what he had let himself in for. Whatever could he make for Gran? He fell asleep, still wondering.

Next morning, Jessica said, "Well, Danny, what's this wonderful present you're going to make?"

"I'm not telling you," said Danny.

"You don't know!" sneered Jessica, but Mum stopped her.

"That's enough, Jessica," she said. "Leave him alone. *Do* you know what you're going to make, Danny?"

"Yes," lied Danny.

"Do you want me to help you?"

"No, thank you," said Danny. Even if he did, he couldn't ask with Jessica sitting there.

"That's all right, then," said Mum, looking more cheerful.

Danny, however, was far from cheerful. He worried about it all over the weekend, but by Monday morning he still had no ideas.

When he got to school, the first thing he saw was a big tub of red clay in the middle of the classroom floor.

Then he remembered they were doing a special project this week. Miss Brown's boyfriend was going to video them all making clay models, to show all the stages they had to go through. Danny had quite forgotten.

Miss Brown said when the models were finished, they would fire them in the kiln, to make them really strong, and then on Friday they would show them to the rest of the school. Then they could take their models home.

It was then that Danny had his brilliant idea. He could make a clay model for Gran. And Jessica wouldn't even see it, so it would be a secret until he gave it to Gran on Saturday.

He looked at the sticky red clay as Miss Brown gave it out, and wondered what to make. What would Gran like?

It was a lovely colour. It reminded him of Rex's coat.

And suddenly he knew what to do.

Gran would like a model of Rex. She could put it on the mantelpiece, beside the little wooden duck she kept there.

Danny asked if he could look in the library for a picture of a dog like Rex. He found one, and stood it on the shelf where he could see it. Then he put on his plastic apron, rolled up his sleeves and set to work.

He liked the feel of the clay squidging through his fingers, though it was quite hard to work with. He hardly noticed Miss Brown's boyfriend walking round the room videoing them all.

By the end of the afternoon, Danny's model was about the right shape, but it didn't look much like Rex yet.

"Put it in a plastic bag, to stop it drying out," said Miss Brown. "You can go on with it tomorrow."

That night Jessica asked him again about Gran's present.

"Where is it, Danny?" she asked.

"It's at school," said Danny.

"What is it, then?" asked Jessica, as if she didn't believe him.

"It's a secret! You'll never guess!"

"Ha!" snorted Jessica, and went back to her homework.

After supper, when Jessica had gone upstairs, Danny asked Mum if they had any photos of Rex.

"I'm sure we have," said Mum. "There's a box of photos in the bottom drawer. What do you want it for?"

"It's for Gran's present, but it's a secret. You won't tell Jessica, will you?"

Mum smiled. "No," she said.

Danny found the box of photos and sat on the

floor looking at them.

There was one of him with Mum, when he was a fat, smiley baby. Jessica was standing beside them, looking rather cross.

There was one of him and Jessica at the seaside, building a sandcastle. Jessica was telling him what to do.

Then he found one of Rex, sitting beside Dad.

Danny knew it was Dad, because Gran had a photo of him on her dresser. But he looked different in this photo. Dad looked nice, he thought. A bit like Jessica, only not so cross. He suddenly wished he could remember more about him.

Danny put the photo carefully in his trouser pocket.

The next day he worked again on his model, with the photo to help him. By the end of the afternoon it was beginning to look like Rex.

Miss Brown was very pleased.

"You have worked hard, Danny," she said.

By Wednesday the model was almost finished. Now he only had to get the feet right, and it would be ready for firing.

That evening Jessica wrapped up the bottle of

bubble bath she had chosen for Gran, and stuck a silver rosette on it.

"That looks beautiful," said Mum. "Gran will be thrilled. How's your present coming on, Danny?"

"It's nearly finished," said Danny.

"Go on, Danny, tell us what it is," said Jessica. But he wouldn't.

By Thursday afternoon it was done. The head was just right, and although the feet were not perfect, Danny decided they would do. Miss Brown showed it to the whole class and said how good it was. He felt very proud.

Then Miss Brown's boyfriend went all round the class with his video camera, filming everyone standing by their models. Danny held up the photo of Rex too.

They all watched as Miss Brown carefully put all the models into the kiln to be fired. She said they would be done by the next morning, ready to show the school in the afternoon. Then they could take them home.

Danny couldn't wait.

But on Friday morning, Miss Brown met him at the door, looking very sad.

"Danny," she said. "I'm so sorry. Something went wrong, and I'm afraid your model exploded in the kiln. It's all in bits. There's nothing we can do with it. After all your hard work, too."

Danny couldn't believe it.

"But you said it would make it stronger!"

Miss Brown looked even sadder. "I'm afraid it does happen sometimes," she said.

Danny felt cold inside. He had been so proud of it, and he just knew Gran would have loved it. And now he had no present for her at all.

He couldn't think of anything else all day. When the others arranged their models on the table in the hall, Danny was too miserable to watch them. Nobody else's model had broken. Only his. It wasn't fair.

In the afternoon the others stood behind their models while the rest of the school walked past and looked at them.

Then Miss Brown told them all to sit down, and she switched on the video.

Danny had forgotten all about the video.

"This is Class 3's project on Clay Modelling," said Miss Brown's voice. "This video shows how a lump of clay becomes a model."

And there on the screen were all the children with their lumps of clay. Danny saw himself grinning as he squeezed the clay in his hands. Miss Brown's voice explained what they were doing as all the models began to take shape.

There was a lot of film of Danny working, and at last he saw himself standing beside the finished model of Rex, holding the photo. The model looked just as good as he remembered it.

Miss Brown's voice said,

"The final stage is firing in the kiln. Sometimes, no matter how careful we are, things can go wrong. Unfortunately, Danny's beautiful model exploded in the kiln. We are so glad we had captured it on video first."

It was then that Danny had his extra-brilliant idea.

Afterwards, he went up to Miss Brown.

"Please, Miss Brown, could I borrow the video?"

Miss Brown smiled. "Did you enjoy it, Danny? Wasn't it a good job we got such a lovely picture of your model before it broke?"

"It was going to be my gran's birthday present. But if I show her the video, at least she can see what it looked like."

Miss Brown thought for a minute. "I've got an even better idea," she said. "My boyfriend will copy the video for you, then you can give her that instead of the model."

"But I haven't got any money," said Danny.

"Oh, it won't cost much to make a copy, Danny. You can have it for nothing. I was so sorry about your lovely model."

Danny could hardly believe his luck.

"Thank you!" he said.

"I'll bring it round this evening," said Miss Brown.

When he got home, Jessica said, "Well, where's your present for Gran? Don't say you've forgotten it!"

"Of course I haven't," said Danny. "Miss Brown's bringing it later."

Mum sighed. "Leaving it till the last minute as usual," she said. "Just like your dad!"

Danny answered the door when Miss Brown came. He took the video, thanked her, and rushed upstairs to wrap it before Jessica could see it.

Straight after breakfast next morning, Mum

hurried them into the car, and they set off for Gran's.

Jessica looked suspiciously at Danny's parcel.

"I don't believe you made it at all," said Jessica.

"Yes I did – well, sort of," said Danny, trying to be truthful. Jessica frowned.

When they got to Gran's, Rex ran out, barking, to meet them. Danny patted his head.

Gran hugged them all, and made them a cup of tea. Then she sat down to open her presents.

She was delighted with the book from Mum, and the bubble bath from Jessica. "Now I can spoil myself," she said. "I can lie in the bath and read my book."

Then she opened Danny's present. Jessica and Mum leaned over to see what it was.

"It's a video," said Mum, with a puzzled frown.

"You cheat! You said you made it!" said Jessica.

Even Gran looked surprised, but she put it in the video player and turned it on.

"It's instead of the present I really made for you," Danny explained.

Then they all watched Danny starting with the ball of red clay, and working on it until it became the model of Rex.

"It looks just like him!" said Gran.

At the end, when Miss Brown explained what had happened to Danny's model, they all said, "Oh, no!"

Then Gran gave Danny a big hug.

"Well, that's a very special present!" she said. "What a shame your model broke, Danny. But never mind, now I can see you making it whenever I want to!"

Mum looked at Danny. "It was a lovely model, Danny," she said, looking surprised and proud. "I had no idea you were so talented!"

Even Jessica looked impressed.

"He certainly is," said Gran. "You're a real craftsman, Danny. Just like your dad!"

Danny looked at her in surprise. "Did Dad make things, too?" he asked.

"Oh, yes," said Gran. "You know my wooden duck on the mantelpiece? Your dad made that when he was just a bit older than you. He was always making models out of odds and ends."

"You're right," said Mum suddenly. "I'd forgotten the things he was good at. I always said you were like him, Danny."

But this time she smiled.

LYNNE BENTON

Lynne Benton was born in Bournemouth but after studying for teacher training in Bath, has lived there ever since. She has four children, and has worked as a teacher in primary schools, a pianist at a dancing school, and now one day a week as a music teacher, which gives her six days a week to be a writer! Her husband, Robin, a fellow teacher, is also a composer, so they understand each other! She reads and writes voraciously, and has had poems and short stories published in magazines, won first prize in a national short story competition, and has two children's books about to be published by Heinemann Educational Press.

She says: "I love the scope for imagination in writing for children, and feel it is vital that children learn to exercise their own imagination. Even in 'realistic' stories they can learn to see the world through another's eyes, which is so important in understanding other people."

The Hippo in the Back Garden

JENNIFER GLEASON

Illustrated by
ANT PARKER

W hen I woke up that morning, I knew
something was going to happen. It
was the first day of the summer
holidays and I had been looking forward to that
day for weeks, if not months. Without school,
anything was possible. There was a different
feeling in the air, as if the wind had shifted
direction to blow away the clouds and bring in a
bright, sunny day, just for me.

I jumped out of bed, threw on my clothes and
gulped down my breakfast. "I'm going out," I
called to my mother.

"Stay out of trouble," she called back, as she
always did.

Just as I walked out the front door, a moving
van pulled up three doors down. The house had
been empty for a long time and someone was

now moving in. As I watched, the moving men started carrying boxes and furniture into the house. I wondered if this family had any kids, especially another boy my age. I thought that I could find a clue in the van. When the men were in the house, I ran up to the van. I crept along the side until I could peer around the back to look inside. Suddenly, the men came back and I had to duck behind the wheel to avoid being seen by them. When they were all back in the house, I looked into the van. Someone tapped me on the shoulder and I nearly jumped out of my skin. I spun around and there was a girl, about my age, standing there. I didn't recognize her.

"Don't do that," I said.

"What are you doing?" she asked.

"I'm trying to find out if there are any kids moving in," I said. I tried to make her leave because she was interfering with my spying. "Leave me alone."

"There's only one kid," she said.

"How do you know?" I asked, annoyed that she could have found out before me, although I had reached the van first.

"I'm the kid," she said. "I'm called Sarah."

I was disappointed that she was a girl and not a boy. "I'm called Pete," I said. "I'd better be going." I turned and started to walk home.

"Would you like to see my hippopotamus?" she asked.

"Your what?" I asked.

"There is a hippo in my back garden," she said. "He's called Pig."

"You can't have a hippo in your back garden," I said. "Hippos only live in African rivers. They have to live in rivers or their skin dries out." We had learned about African animals in school.

"But this hippo lives in my back garden," said Sarah. "He's from my Aunt Sophie in Africa. At my old house we lived near the zoo. I used to go there to see the hippo. I wrote to my Aunt Sophie about how much I would miss the hippo when we moved. She sent me one."

"I don't believe you," I said.

"Then see for yourself," she said and turned to go into the house. I followed her indoors, stepped around the boxes lining the hallway, walked through the kitchen and went out the back door. We walked to the end of the garden, and there, sitting in a flower-bed, calmly munching on irises, was a hippo.

I couldn't believe my eyes. She had been telling the truth! The hippo wasn't very big; about the size of a large dog. He looked up, grunted at us and then continued to eat the flowers.

"He's very small for a hippo," I said.

"He's a pigmy hippo," said Sarah, "and he's not full grown."

A lady walked out of the house towards us. "Pig isn't eating the flowers, is he?" she asked. "Sarah, can't you get your hippo to eat the weeds and not the flowers?" She then turned to me. "Who is this?" she asked.

"This is my friend Pete," said Sarah. I squirmed because I wasn't quite sure that I wanted to be friends with this girl yet. She did have a cool hippo though, and she didn't seem too bad, for a girl.

"Hello," I said. "It's a very nice hippo." The hippo moved into the shade of a tree and started rolling around in the dirt. "How long have you had him?" I asked.

"He arrived yesterday," said Sarah.

"He's already eaten all of the grass under the

tree and many of the flowers," said Sarah's mother. "We'll have to build a pen for him so that he can't get to the flowers."

"He won't like a pen," said Sarah. "I want him to be able to walk around the garden."

"We'll discuss it later," said Sarah's mother. "Just keep him out of the flowers for now." She turned to walk back into the house.

"That means that she'll put him in a pen," sighed Sarah.

"I don't think he's too happy," I said. He was rolling around and covering himself with dirt but he didn't look right. "I bet he's too dry. He really needs mud."

"There's a hose-pipe," said Sarah. "Maybe we should spray him."

We got the hose-pipe and started spraying Pig. The dirt quickly turned to mud. Pig rolled until he was completely covered with a thick layer of mud. He then yawned, closed his eyes and grunted happily.

"That helped," I said. "Perhaps he should be sprayed several times a day." Sarah nodded in agreement. We then went back into the house where Sarah's mother made us sandwiches. As soon as we finished lunch, we ran back out to see Pig. He was sitting in another flower-bed munching on begonias. "No, bad Pig!" scolded Sarah. "Stop that or Mum will put you in a pen!" Sarah tried to pull the hippo out of the flower-bed. "He's very heavy."

I helped to pull Pig out and we kept him away from the flowers. He ran away from us, over to the other side of the garden, and started chewing on other flowers. We spent the rest of the afternoon keeping Pig out of the flower-beds and spraying him with water when he sat in the mud. At teatime, he settled down, yawned and appeared to go to sleep. I promised to return the next day to help keep Pig out of the flowers. I ran home before my mother was angry with me for being late.

"What happened to you?" asked Mum. "You're all wet and muddy."

"I've been chasing a hippo," I said.

"Don't lie to me," said Mum. "I know that you've been playing in the stream again. Do you always have to fall in and get so wet and dirty?"

"I didn't go there," I almost said, but I knew she wouldn't believe me. I didn't want to be punished and not able to see Pig. "I'll stay out of the stream," I said instead.

"OK, then," said Mum. "I'll let you off this time. Go and wash your hands for tea."

The next day, I hurriedly ate breakfast. Mum yelled, "Stay out of the stream today!" as I ran out the door and over to Sarah's. When Sarah came to the door she looked sad.

"They're building a pen for Pig," she said.

"But we kept him out of the flowers," I said.

"Yes," said Sarah, "but he ate all of the flowers last night." It was then that I remembered that hippos are more active at night. They try to stay wet and cool during the day but eat during the night. I followed Sarah into the back garden. It had been destroyed. All the flowers had been eaten, leaving just rows of stalks. There were holes in the flower-bed where Pig had dug up roots and several of the bushes had been knocked over. It looked as if a steamroller had run through the garden. Pig was sitting in his muddy wallow, yawning and grunting contentedly as Sarah's parents built a pen around him. That day wasn't nearly as much fun. We watered Pig now and then and looked at him sitting in his mud.

The following morning, as I was walking down the stairs for breakfast, there was a knock on the door. My mother opened it and there stood Sarah. "Please," she said, "is Pete home? I've lost Pig."

"He hasn't had his breakfast yet," said my mum. "He can't come out yet even if you've lost your pig."

"But it's important," she said. "I'm really worried what he might do. Pete knows the town better than me and should be able to help me find him."

"Please, Mum," I said. "Can't I just take a piece of toast and go?" Mum looked doubtful but finally said OK. I ran out to Sarah. "What happened?"

"Pig got out of the back garden," she said. "Where could he have gone?"

I wasn't sure. "What do hippos like?" I asked.

"Rivers and mud," said Sarah.

"There aren't any rivers here," I said, "but there is a stream. Come on, I'll show you where it is." We ran down the street towards the stream. When we reached the stream, there were several older kids playing there, splashing in the water and looking for newts.

"Have you seen a hippo?" asked Sarah. The other kids laughed.

"She thinks hippos live in streams," said one kid. "Isn't that funny?"

"There's nothing bigger than a frog here," said another, "except for the great white shark! Be careful it doesn't eat you." They all started laughing again.

"Come on, Sarah," I said. "Don't pay any attention to them." We started walking up the stream. There wasn't any sign of Pig. Sarah jumped across the stream on some rocks and we walked up and down the banks calling "Pig!" After half an hour we had followed the stream as far as we could in both directions and there was still no sign of Pig. We climbed on to a bridge that crossed the stream and walked back towards home along the road. "What else do hippos like?" I asked.

"Well," said Sarah, "Pig likes flowers."

"There's a flower garden in the centre of

town," I said. "Maybe he went there." We ran through the streets until we came to the garden. We looked into every flower-bed for Pig. We asked everyone we saw if they had seen a small hippo, but they just gave us strange looks or told us that hippos are only found in Africa.

"Here, Pig!" I called.

"Pig, where are you?" called Sarah.

Pig wasn't there either.

We walked slowly back to Sarah's house, trying to think where else we would go if we were hippos. As we started to walk down our street we heard a scream. "That came from Mrs Jenkins' house," I said. "She has a pond in her back garden."

"That's probably where Pig is," said Sarah.

We ran to Mrs Jenkins' house just as she came out exclaiming, "There's a monster in my back garden!" We slipped into Mrs Jenkins' back garden as she went to find her neighbour for help.

The pond was in the middle of the garden and sitting in the middle of the pond was Pig. Just his eyes and ears stuck out of the water as he happily chewed pond reeds and water lilies. When he

saw us he picked up his head, yawned and grunted at us.

"What are you doing, Pig?" scolded Sarah. "You shouldn't be in there."

"We have to get him out before Mrs Jenkins comes back," I said. "What should we do?"

"We'll pull him out," she said. "You pull on one side and I'll push on the other."

I started to pull as Sarah pushed. Pig just grunted and continued to eat the water plants. He didn't move at all. "It's not working," I said. "Push harder." Sarah gave a big push and fell into the pond. I started laughing because she looked so funny sitting in the pond covered with plants. Pig suddenly turned towards her and I lost my balance. I fell in and Sarah started laughing. Pig decided that the pond was too crowded and climbed out. We were laughing so hard that we almost didn't notice that he was heading for the garden gate.

"Quick!" shouted Sarah. "We have to get him home." We jumped out of the pond and caught up with Pig on the street. We herded him to Sarah's house. The front door was open and Pig ran into the house.

"Get that hippo out of the house!" yelled Sarah's mum. Rather than running straight through and into the back garden, Pig turned and went into the lounge. He jumped up on the sofa which had a flowered cover. He sat down and grunted happily. "That does it!" said Sarah's mum. "The hippo has to go. You can have a cat instead, like a normal child."

"Poor Pig," said Sarah. "I'll miss you."

"I will too," I said.

We pulled Pig off the sofa but he got away from us. He knocked over a lamp and ran into the kitchen. "Come on, Pete," yelled Sarah. We chased him around the kitchen table until that too turned over. Pig was so startled that he ran out the back door and straight into his pen. Sarah quickly closed the gate. "Safe at last," she said. Pig settled into his mud and grunted. We tied the gate in several places to make sure that there was no way that he could ever get out again.

Pig was sent back to Africa, where hippos belong. Sarah wrote to her Aunt Sophie to thank her very much for the hippo and to tell her how much fun we had with Pig. Sarah said she was sorry that she wasn't able to keep Pig. She told her aunt that she was greatly looking forward to getting a cat because that would be much less trouble.

One day Sarah knocked on the door. When I opened it she said, "My Aunt Sophie wrote back. She says that Pig is very happy back in Africa."

"That's good," I said.

"Do you want to come over and see my new cat?" she said. "Well, it's not a full-grown cat yet, it's just a cub."

"Baby cats are called kittens," I said. "Everyone knows that."

"Yes," she said, "I know, but this one is a cub. Aunt Sophie sent it. You see, there is a lion in my back garden."

THE HIPPO IN THE BACK GARDEN

JENNIFER GLEASON

Jennifer Gleason was born in Michigan, USA, but since recently completing her PhD in Biology, has been dividing her time between Fife, where she is a research fellow at the University of St Andrews; and Manchester, where her boyfriend Martin lives. She loves to travel, and also enjoys reading, knitting, photography, gardening, hiking and camping. Apart from technical articles, "The Hippo in the Back Garden" is her first piece of published fiction.

She says: "I don't have any children but I have a very young half-sister. Because I now live in Britain, I am far away from her. Writing a story is a way that I can play with her from a distance."

Don't Mention Boats in Our House

Richard Newton

Illustrated by

Nick Sharratt

To Hollie and Alice. Fair weather sailors,
all weather friends.

I f you ever come round to our house for tea
(and I don't see why you should, because
you're not even in my school, let alone my
class), but if you do come round, don't mention
boats, not in front of my dad anyway.

Boats haven't been spoken of since last summer, which is a pity really, seeing as how we live
on the edge of Poole Harbour which is the second
biggest natural harbour in the world. (Sydney
Harbour in Australia is the biggest, but I expect
you knew that already.) There are boats every-
where. Fishing boats, tug boats, cargo boats,
lifeboats, speedboats, rowing boats and sailing
boats. There are big ferry boats that go to France,
little ferry boats that go to Brownsea Island and a
car ferry that goes across the harbour to Shell Bay.
But we don't talk about any of them any more.

Last year we did. In fact my dad didn't just talk about them, he decided it would be a good idea to have a boat all of our own.

That caused the problem.

"It'll be just like *Swallows and Amazons*," he said. I looked at my sister and started giggling. *Swallows and Amazons* is an old book about a bunch of kids who had a boat. Mum had started to read it to us once, but only until we found out that one of the girls in the book is called Titty. Of course we just cracked up and Mum went ballistic and that was the end of that. So when I started giggling at Dad, Mum gave me one of her LOOKS.

"We'll get a little sailing dinghy," said Dad, "then we can go swimming in Shell Bay or picnicking on Brownsea Island without having to pay for the ferry."

"But you can't sail," says Mum.

"It's easy," says Dad. "People have been doing it for hundreds of years."

You'd think he'd know better at his age. And him a policeman too. But no. He came home a few evenings later, towing a trailer behind his car. And on the trailer was a little blue sailing boat. On the back of the boat in yellow letters was the boat's name. *Pan Nick*.

"Well, what do you think?" Dad asks Mum.

"I think it's a very good name," says Mum.

Dad was very excited about our new boat, and he couldn't wait to get it into the water. In fact he decided we would launch it that Saturday.

"But you're supposed to be on duty on Saturday," says Mum. "You're directing the traffic in the town centre."

"I told Chief Inspector Nabbit that an important family matter had come up, so I'd have to take the day off."

"That's not a very good example to set the children," says Mum.

Dad put on his obstinate look and said that launching *Pan Nick was* an important family matter.

Saturday was sunny, warm and breezy. The public slipway where people put their boats into the harbour was only a mile from our house, so it didn't take long to tow the boat there.

"Don't you think it's a bit too breezy?" asks Mum.

"You can't sail a boat without wind," says Dad.

The slipway was a concrete ramp that sloped down into the water. But when we got there, it didn't slope into the water. It sloped into the mud. The edge of the water was about fifty metres away. An old sailor leaned over the wall at the top of the slipway.

"Tide's out," he said. "You'll have to wait a couple of hours for the water to come in."

"No need," says Dad. "It's only a little boat – doesn't weigh very much. We'll manage."

The old sailor looked at our boat, then he looked at the distant water, then he looked at Dad. "Suit yourself," he said.

When Dad makes up his mind to do something, nothing will stop him. Nothing apart from harbour mud, that is. He unhitched the trailer from the back of the car and pushed it down the slipway. As soon as it reached the end of the concrete, the trailer sank without trace into the thick, black, smelly mud, leaving the boat sitting on the surface. Unfortunately Dad was still holding on to the trailer, and he was now up to his waist in the evil-smelling muck.

The old sailor threw him a rope and hauled him out. "Done much sailing?" he asked. Dad just glared at him and said nothing.

"Let's go home while we wait for the tide to come in," says Mum. So we all got back into the car, and drove home with all the windows open to get rid of the stink.

Two hours later we were back at the slipway. Dad was in clean clothes, the water was lapping halfway up the slipway and our boat was floating. Unfortunately it was floating some distance away from the shore, Dad having forgotten to tie it up. He said something that would have lost me my pocket money for a month if *I'd* said it. We watched helplessly as *Pan Nick* bobbed further and further out of reach.

Just then the old sailor appeared round the harbour wall, rowing an old boat. "The tide's come in then," he said. Dad nodded.

"Give me ten quid and I'll get your boat back."

"Ten quid? That's daylight robbery!"

"Piracy actually," said the sailor, looking rather offended. "Well, do you want her back or not?"

Dad swore under his breath, then pulled a ten-pound note out of his pocket and shoved it into the sailor's outstretched hand. A few minutes later, *Pan Nick* was safely tied up to the slipway and we all climbed in.

By now the breeze had got stronger, blowing across the water of the harbour, making little waves that splashed against the side of the boat. Mum was looking a bit nervous, but me and my sister thought it was good fun. We all put our life jackets on and waited for Dad to tell us what to do. He was standing in the middle of the boat holding on to some ropes and looking up at the top of the mast. "We've just got to get the sail up and away we go," he said.

He started pulling on one of the ropes and sure enough, the sail started going up the mast. It was flapping madly in the wind and making a tremendous noise.

"Watch out for the boom!" shouts Dad.

"What's the boom?" we yelled.

"It's the wooden pole at the bottom of the sail. If the wind catches it, it could slam across the boat and knock you into the—"

At that moment a particularly strong gust of wind caught the sail, and a long, heavy piece of wood attached to the bottom of it swept across the boat. Mum, my sister and me all ducked, and the boom whistled over our heads. It caught Dad right in the stomach. He yelled and fell overboard with a tremendous splash. Luckily we were very close to the shore and the water was only waist deep. But he still managed to go right under, and when he stood up, he started sinking in the mud. He scrambled quickly back into the boat, losing one of his shoes in the process. He said another word that I wouldn't dare repeat.

"Are you sure you know what you're doing?" asked Mum.

Dad just grunted. He finished pulling up the sail, grabbed the tiller and steered away from the shore. Nothing happened.

"Shall I untie you?" The old sailor pointed to the rope still securing *Pan Nick* to the slipway.

Dad scowled and nodded. The old sailor unhitched the rope and threw it on board. Immediately the wind filled the sail and *Pan Nick* shot off across the harbour like a race horse. The wind seemed to be doing its best to blow us over, so Dad told us to lean out over the side to balance the boat. Mum began to go green and my

sister started crying. I couldn't see the problem. I thought this was the most exciting feeling in the world. The spray, the wind in my face, the rush of water under the boat, the way that Brownsea Island seemed to be racing towards us…

"Dad!"

"Not now. Can't you see I'm trying to concentrate?"

Why do grown-ups always think that kids have nothing important to say? I was trying to tell him that we were getting very close to the old wooden jetty that sticks out from the shore of the island.

"But Dad!"

"I said not … aargh! … Ready about, ready about!"

Apparently "Ready about" means "Stand by, we're going to turn round." Goodness knows why boats have to have their own language. They don't have left sides and right sides, they have port and starboard. They don't have front and back, they have fore and aft. And they don't measure their speed in miles per hour, they measure it in knots. It's all very confusing.

Anyway, if Dad had said, "Hold tight, I'm

going to turn," we might have been ready. As it was, we weren't. Suddenly the boat spun round and the wind was coming from the opposite side. Unfortunately my mum, my sister and me were still leaning out on the side of the dinghy that was now dipping into the water. You can guess what happened. *Pan Nick* went right over and tipped us all into the harbour.

"Everybody hang on to the boat!" Dad yelled, after we'd coughed and spluttered our way to the surface. "We'll try and get her upright again."

Well, we tried, but what with the wind and the strong current, we just couldn't get *Pan Nick* back up. What's more, the current seemed to be carrying us towards the harbour entrance.

"People have been doing this for hundreds of years, I suppose," Mum shouted to Dad, rather unhelpfully, I thought.

"Don't worry," said Dad, "the harbour is filled with boats. Someone will see us soon and rescue us."

He was right. Before very long a fast launch sped towards us. As it came nearer we could see men on the deck wearing blue uniforms. One man, obviously in charge, was pointing and shouting something. Dad suddenly went white.

"Oh, no . . ."

"What's the matter?" asked Mum. "Aren't you glad to be rescued? I know *I* am."

"So am I," said my sister. "I don't like this horrid boat. I don't like being in the water. I don't like sailing. I want to go home."

Dad didn't seem at all happy to be saved. "Of all the boats in Poole Harbour, why did we have to be rescued by *that* one?" He pointed to the name on the side of the launch. It was called *The Alarm*.

"What's so special about *The Alarm*?" I asked.

"Oh, nothing," said Dad. "It's only the police patrol boat, that's all."

"That's nice," said Mum. "I expect some of your friends are on board."

"I can see who's on board. That man waving his arms about and shouting is Chief Inspector Nabbit. My boss."

The police soon got us on board *The Alarm* and wrapped us in blankets. Dad got plenty of stick from his mates, and a real earful from Chief Inspector Nabbit. *Pan Nick* was towed back to the slipway where the old sailor helped Dad pull the trailer out of the mud and get the boat back on to it. He only wanted fifty quid for helping. Dad told him to keep the boat instead.

Chief Inspector Nabbit put Dad on Saturday morning traffic duty for the rest of the summer. Mum and my sister didn't speak to him for the rest of the weekend. I couldn't see what all the fuss was about. I'd had a great time. I especially enjoyed the trip back across the harbour in the police launch. I asked Dad if we could have a speed boat next time, but he told me there wasn't going to be a next time. And if I ever mentioned boats to him again, he'd stop my pocket money for a year. Parents can be so unreasonable.

That's why, if you ever come round to our house, you must never *ever* mention ... those things that float on the water.

RICHARD NEWTON

Richard Newton was born in Poole, Dorset, and lives there now. He is married to Sonia and has two girls – Hollie, aged fourteen, and Alice, aged eleven. He studied Psychology and English at London University and had various jobs before becoming a commercial producer at a radio station in Portsmouth. He is now freelance, working on radio, press and TV commercials. His story "Uncle Jim" was a winner of the 1989 Ian St James Awards, and was published in an anthology. His hobby is sailing!

He says: "Before our two daughters could read for themselves (and for a good while after!) Sonia and I made a point of reading bedtime stories to them. Apart from being an enjoyable time spent together, it helped them realize that books are fun and entertainment doesn't have to come from a TV screen.

"Children hate to be patronized, love to laugh at grown-ups and above all, like a good story. They are also brutally honest when asked for their opinion. I let Hollie and Alice read this story before I entered it. The fact that they didn't dismiss it out of hand I took as a great compliment and a good omen."

The Miracle of
Little Abdul Bashir

RICHARD
NATHANSON

Illustrated by
JULIE ANDERSON

From the author:

It is really Abdul who wrote this story. You would have liked him very much. His face would not have shocked you because in it, you would have seen his wonderful spirit and courage.

The world is full of amazing people of every age. And full of the most amazing stories about them. They are all around you – waiting to be written.

Why not write about the people you know and the extraordinary, funny, even sad things you have seen – adding whatever your imagination tells you?

For Abdul

T his is the story
of a very brave little boy
called Abdul Bashir.

Abdul was born in Afghanistan
in a village called Mohammedagar
high in the mountains.

The houses were white and square
and very simple.

One afternoon
when Abdul was only six weeks old
and asleep in his cot,
the dark and frightening shadow
of what at first seemed like
a giant whirring mosquito,
fell across the village.

The people looked up
and saw a helicopter.
But it was no ordinary helicopter.
And its sound was angry and cruel.

Suddenly from it dropped
a black and pointed shape.

For a moment there was silence.
And then a terrible explosion.

The village seemed to break
into a thousand pieces.
The air was filled with smoke,
and flames
and the screaming of children.

Many were hurt,
and some were killed.

Little Abdul's house shook
and collapsed.

Flames surrounded him
as he lay
trapped and screaming in his cot.

His father ran into the house
and pulled him free.

Abdul was alive.

But his face had disappeared,
burnt away by the flames.

Abdul's mother and father
knew that soldiers would soon come
to take people prisoner,
and perhaps even kill them.

They wrapped Abdul in a blanket
and fled from the village.

Perhaps you remember the name
of another baby boy
whose mother and father
carried him away from death.

For ten days,
they travelled by night,
when it was cooler and less dangerous.
And by day, they slept.

It was a terrible journey
across the mountains.

Abdul was in great pain;
and he nearly died.

But God gave Abdul's father and mother
great strength.

And to Abdul,
He gave the greatest strength of all.
For He wanted Abdul very much to live;
and to be able to help the other children
in his country,
who had been hurt
by the falling bombs
and by the soldiers.

At last, they arrived at a refugee camp
on the border of Pakistan.

There, by happy chance,
was visiting a famous English pop star.

When he saw Abdul,
he was so upset that he
gave Mr and Mrs Bashir
the money to fly to London;
where he knew there was a wonderful doctor
who could help Abdul become better.

How strange life is, thought Mr and Mrs Bashir
as they sat in the plane
to England.

One moment, we are in our little village
and the next, we are flying to a country
whose language we neither speak
nor understand,
and where we know nobody.

The doctor worked
in Queen Mary's Hospital, Roehampton,
a leafy part of London
near Richmond Park.

When he saw Abdul
he told Mr and Mrs Bashir
that Abdul would need many operations
to make him see and eat properly
and for his face
to once again look like a face.

Abdul's first operations were very painful.
But afterwards, he was able to see and eat
a little more easily.

Abdul and his parents
lived in a small flat near the hospital,
in a place called Putney.

His mother and father
spoke only a few words of English,
and they knew very few people.
Their life was difficult and lonely.

People looked at Abdul and looked away
because they were frightened
and because they didn't know what to say.

It was also very expensive

for Abdul and his parents to live in Putney
and to visit the hospital.

And they were told
that they would have to go back to Afghanistan
because there was not enough money
for them to stay.

But Abdul's parents
were very unhappy about this.
Because in Afghanistan
there was no doctor
who could help Abdul.
And because the war had not stopped
and they might all face death.

Then a miracle happened.

One morning,
when almost all their money had gone,
Mr Bashir and Abdul
went to the supermarket for bread.
It was a very big place
with many people coming and going.
But no one stopped to say hello.

As they were leaving,
a lady called Mary
appeared in front of Abdul's pram
and looked at him.

Her eyes filled with tears,
and she could not speak.
She wanted to ask what had happened
and how she could help.
But she was so shocked
that no words came.

That night Mary had a dream.

She dreamt that God had chosen Abdul
to help other children in Afghanistan
who had also been hurt by the war.
And that God
wanted her to help Abdul.

The next day
she called together all her friends.
And they decided to raise
as much money as possible
to help Abdul stay in England.

The local newspaper wrote a big article
with a photograph of Abdul.
And when The Children of Putney
saw Abdul's poor burnt away little face
and read that he did not have enough money
to stay in Putney,
they called a special meeting.

And they had a brilliant idea.
And like many brilliant ideas
it was very simple.

Every boy and girl in Putney
would ask their parents and their grandparents
and their friends
to give them money for Abdul
in exchange for doing good work at school
for running competitions of every kind
including walking around their bedroom
eighty times
with a tangerine on their heads
with a straight back
and for looking after their small brothers
and sisters
and for doing

a hundred other valuable and interesting things.

But perhaps you have an idea
no one else has yet thought of ... ?

Then another wonderful thing happened.

A famous newsreader on English television
heard about Abdul
and how The Children of Putney
were helping him.

And he decided to make a
television programme about Abdul.

Children all over England and Scotland,
Wales and Ireland saw that programme.

And they wrote saying
that they also wanted to do
what The Children of Putney were doing
and to help Abdul stay and get better.

And The Children of Scotland and Ireland,
Wales and England

sent so many letters with money
that the postman had to deliver them
in a big lorry
with a policeman sitting on top
to guard all the money.

And then
the British government sent Abdul
a large and important-looking letter.

It said
that he could stay in England
until he was better.
And that he would not have to pay
for his operations any longer.

When The Children of Ireland and Wales,
Scotland and England
heard this exciting news,
they telephoned Mary
and asked her to use the money
they were raising
to also build a hospital in Afghanistan
for other children like Abdul
who had been badly burnt in the war.

And that, dear reader,
is how The Abdul Bashir Hospital
came – miraculously – to be built.
And how one very brave little boy
was able
in a strange and unknown country
without saying a word
to save the lives
of many other little boys and girls
in his own land.

Abdul's operations continued
yet, with each operation
his heart grew weaker.

His Spirit
saw the wonderful work
his friends were doing for him
and for The Children of Afghanistan.
And his Spirit knew it could – at last –
leave the burnt and scarred body
it had lived in those four terrible years.

One beautiful sunlit afternoon
in the middle of one of his many operations

Abdul's heart stopped beating for ever.
But his Spirit lives on
in the hearts
of his many friends.
Asking them to continue
their life-saving work.

RICHARD NATHANSON

Richard Nathanson was born in London and lives in Putney, with his artist wife Victoria and their three children. He is a Fine Art advisor, a producer and distributor of programmes about education, health and disability, an originator of "non-mainstream" advertising poster concepts, and an author. Favourite pastimes include visual art in all its forms, reading, photography, tennis and discovering unspoilt corners of beauty in his own back yard and beyond. He has had two books for adults published, as well as numerous art exhibition catalogues.

He says: "I think children have, from a surprisingly early age, an intuitive sense of certain realities in life. Mysteriously this co-exists with, and possibly enhances, a child's sense and need of wonder and magic and humour. As children respond quite naturally to music, so do they to the music of language. And it is the collective rhythm of words, together with the story they tell – and the imagery they conjure up – which can produce a spellbound emotional response."

Perfect Pets

BRENDA SIVERS

Illustrated by
PHILIP REEVE

To Caroline Hatwell, who approved it.

E very Saturday and most evenings after school William helped in his father's pet shop, which was called Perfect Pets.

Now most pet shops sell furry creatures in cages and brightly-coloured fish in tanks and pretty songbirds – but not Perfect Pets, as people soon found out.

"I'm looking for a dear little puppy to give my grandson for his birthday," an elderly lady said to William one Saturday morning.

"I'm sorry," said William. "We don't sell dogs."

"Oh well, I'll have to get him a dear little kitten then."

But William shook his head. "We don't sell cats either."

"No dogs or cats?" exclaimed the lady in

amazement. "But I thought this was a pet shop."

"It is," said William. "We sell perfect pets. Come and look." And he led her to a large tank at the back of the shop.

"Ugh!" cried the lady, peering in. "Are they huge worms or small snakes?"

"Neither," said William. "They're eels."

"Eels? Nobody has an eel for a pet."

"Of course they do. We've sold hundreds of them."

"Oh, I don't know..." The lady shook her head.

"Let me introduce you to one," said William, reaching into the tank and pulling out a particularly long, fat eel that writhed and slithered like a piece of wet rubber. "This is Rebecca. Rebecca, this is ... I'm sorry, I don't know your name."

"Mrs Fry," said the lady.

"She's pleased to meet you," said William.

"She's not exactly cuddly, is she?" said Mrs Fry, looking at Rebecca doubtfully. "I mean, you can't stroke her or tickle her tummy, can you?"

"Of course you can. She loves it. Just try tickling her behind her ears."

Mrs Fry stretched out her hand and then she hesitated.

"Er ... where exactly are her ears?"

"To be honest she doesn't have any," admitted William, "but tickle her behind where her ears would be if she had them."

Screwing up her courage, Mrs Fry tickled the eel behind her imaginary ears and Rebecca wagged her tail and purred.

"You see," said William, "she likes you."

"Does she?"

"Oh, yes. She wants to give you a kiss."

Rebecca puckered her lips but Mrs Fry backed away.

"No, I still don't think she's the right kind of pet for my grandson, thank you," she said.

"She's house-trained," said William, who was a very determined salesman, "and obedient too. She walks to heel and she sits and lies down on command."

"Does she do tricks?"

"Does she do *tricks*? Just watch this. OK, Rebecca," cried William holding out a hoop. "Get ready, steady ... Go!"

The eel leaped into the air, shot through the

hoop and landed with a wet plop! on the other side.

"Now sit up for the lady," said William, holding out a biscuit, and the eel reared up and begged.

"Now play dead!"

The eel rolled over on to her back, closed her eyes and stopped breathing.

Mrs Fry was impressed. "How much is she?" she asked.

"Only a pound," said William, "and for that I'll throw in a collar and lead for her and a feeding bowl."

"Is she a finicky eater?"

"No, she'll eat anything you eat – scrambled eggs on toast for breakfast, sausages and baked beans for tea. But don't let her have too many sweets or chocolates. They bring her out in spots."

"All right," said Mrs Fry. "I'll take her."

It was always a sad moment for William when he had to say goodbye to one of his beloved eels and he threw his arms round Rebecca and hugged her tightly.

"Goodbye, old friend," he said. "And good luck."

The lady put the collar and lead on Rebecca and the eel followed her obediently out of the shop, pausing at the door to wave farewell to William and blow him a last kiss.

"I sold Rebecca to a very nice lady," William told his father later that morning.

"I only hope she'll look after her properly," said his father. "I'm worried that people aren't giving their eels enough exercise. In fact, I don't think they're giving them any exercise. And there's nothing worse than a lazy eel. They just lie around the house all day, sleeping or watching television."

William thought about what his father had said and he realized it was true. He never saw any eels out for a walk. He never saw them in the park, chasing balls or fetching sticks. He never saw them digging up flower-beds or burying bones. It was most odd.

And then one day he discovered the dreadful truth.

A small boy came into Perfect Pets, crying bitterly.

"What's wrong with you?" demanded William.

"I've lost Sophie, my pet eel," sobbed the boy. "My aunt bought her for me for Christmas and now she's g . . . gone."

"Run away, you mean?"

"No, she didn't run away. She's inside my g . . . grandpa."

"Inside your g . . . grandpa?" echoed William in disbelief. "How on earth did she get inside him?"

"I'd just tucked her up in her cot for the night and told her a bedtime story," explained the boy, "when Grandpa came in. Sophie leaped up and scuttled over to him, because she was a very friendly little thing, but Grandpa shouted, "Eels, my favourite food!" and before she could bark for help he grabbed her and put her in a saucepan of boiling water."

William was so shocked he couldn't speak. He remembered Sophie very well. She had been a really pretty eel with big blue eyes and the cutest little smile.

"So that's why I never see any of our eels around," sighed William. "Everybody's eating them."

The boy nodded. "Eel burgers are all the craze now."

"But how could anyone do such a horrible thing?"

"Because eels are delicious, my grandpa says," said the boy. "And he'd like another one, please, but a bit fatter this time. There wasn't much meat on Sophie." And he held up a pound coin.

"Get out!" shouted William, chasing him from the shop.

His father was just as angry when William told him.

"I'm selling up," he said. "I'm not wasting my time raising perfect pets just for people to eat."

"But what will you do with all the ones you've got left, dear?" asked William's mother.

"I'll have to put them to sleep."

"Oh Dad, no!" William was aghast. "You can't do that. Why can't they live up here in the flat with us?"

"Because we don't have a garden, do we? Where would they exercise? We couldn't take fifty eels to the park every day! And where would they relieve themselves?"

"On my carpets, probably," said William's mother, frowning.

William slept badly that night. He couldn't

stop thinking about the fate that awaited the poor little eels. His father would put on their leads and they'd all get terribly excited, thinking they were going for a nice long walk, and then . . .

He buried his face in the pillow and was just about to burst into tears when he suddenly had a marvellous idea.

I'll take them back to the sea, he thought. Once they're in the water they'll be safe.

The next morning, before his parents were awake, William crept down the stairs and went into the shop. All the eels were still fast asleep, snoring gently, and they were a bit annoyed when he prodded them awake.

"I've got some bad news for you," he whispered.

When William told them what his father was going to do, they huddled round him, trembling.

"Don't worry," he said. "I'm going to take you all back to the sea. Nobody will be able to get you there."

The eels were so pleased, they cheered and slapped William on the back, but he put his finger to his lips and said, "Sssssssh! Don't wake

Mum and Dad. Now come on, we're going down to the station to get on a train."

Fortunately it was very early in the morning and there was nobody about so they could get to the station without trouble. But then William's problems began.

"Where d'you want to go?" asked the man at the ticket office.

"To the seaside," said William.

"Which seaside?"

"Any seaside."

"You can't buy a ticket for any seaside. You've got to tell me which seaside."

"The nearest."

"That'll be Brighton," said the man. "How many tickets d'you want?"

"About fifty."

"You can't have about fifty. You can have forty-nine or fifty or fifty-one. Which d'you want?"

"I'll have to count them," said William. And he clapped his hands to get the eels' attention because they were all chattering excitedly amongst themselves.

"Everyone get in line, please. As quickly as

you can!" he shouted above the din. So the eels all lined up and William counted them. But the very young ones were in a silly mood and kept squirming in and out of the queue and hiding, so that the first time William counted twenty-six and the second time two hundred and forty-one.

"Anyone who misbehaves will be left behind," he said angrily.

At that the baby eels stopped fooling around and stood in an orderly line.

"There are thirty-eight adults, twelve babies and me," William said to the man in the ticket office.

"Thirty-eight adults, twelve babies and you..." The man did a quick calculation. "That comes to two hundred pounds exactly."

William's mouth fell open. Two hundred pounds! He'd never had that much money in his life.

"I've only got twenty-three pounds and fifty-four pence," he said, which was the money his father had given him for working in the shop.

"Then you can't go on the train, can you?" said the man.

"Isn't there a cheaper way to travel?" William asked hopefully. "Is it cheaper to stand?"

"No, it isn't."

"We could ride on the roof."

"No, you couldn't."

"What about if we sat on the bumpers?"

"Not allowed."

"Not even at half price?"

"Not at any price."

"But we've got to get to Brighton."

"Well, why don't you hitch a lift?" said the man.

William's parents had always warned him not to hitchhike because it could be dangerous but he knew it was his only hope of getting the eels to Brighton, so he gathered them up and took them down to the motorway.

They stood there for ages waving at cars and trucks while William shouted, "Brighton, please! Take us to Brighton!"

A van with "Fresh Fish" on the side pulled up but William decided it would be unwise to accept the driver's offer of a lift.

Finally a small car stopped and the man driving it said, "Brighton? Well, what luck. I'm going there. Hop in."

It was a tight squeeze for thirty-eight adult eels, twelve babies, a man and a boy but if everybody breathed in and tried not to breathe out they could just get the door shut.

The eels were so excited they all started singing loudly and some of the babies behaved very badly, making rude signs and sticking their tongues out at passing cars until William told them to stop it or else.

He told the man why they were going to the sea and the man agreed it was quite disgusting the way people kept eating dear little eels ... but William couldn't help noticing that every time the man looked at the eels on the back seat his eyes lit up in a very greedy way and he drooled so much he had to keep dabbing at his mouth with a handkerchief.

"I'm sorry, I'm not going right to the front," he said, "but I could drop you off in town, if that's OK."

"That's very kind of you," said William. But as he and the eels got out he noticed a pair of tiny eyes peering helplessly out of the man's coat pocket.

"Hey!" cried William. "You've got Toby in your pocket."

"Toby? Well, well, so I have," said the man, pretending to be surprised. "I wonder how he got in there?"

"And Toby says you've got his sister Lucy up your sleeve," said William as the eel leaped into his arms, crying.

Looking very guilty, the man handed over Toby's sister and drove off.

"You see," William said to the eels, "that just shows you can never be too careful. That man pretended to love you but he'd really only love you in a bun with tomato and ketchup, so stay very close to me while we walk through these busy streets if you don't want to end up as somebody's snack."

Despite his warning, however, the eels reared up on their tails, sniffing the air eagerly, and as soon as they got a whiff of the briny smell of the ocean they galloped off, barking madly.

"All right, in you go!" cried William when they got there. "Into the water!"

But the eels hung their heads and looked

embarrassed because they'd all forgotten to bring their swimsuits.

It cost William almost all of his twenty-three pounds and fifty-four pence to buy swimsuits for thirty-eight adult eels and twelve babies, and then they took ages making up their minds what colours they liked.

They wanted bathing caps as well, but William said it didn't matter if they got their hair wet, and some of the babies wanted water-wings because they hadn't yet learned to swim properly. And, of course, when they got out of the shop they were all hungry.

"I've only got a pound left and I'll need that to get home," said William. "And, anyway, once you're in the sea you'll find all kinds of lovely things to eat."

The eels wanted to know what kinds of lovely things and William told a few porkies, saying they'd find pizzas floating on the water and cream cakes . . .

After that they couldn't wait to jump in.

William found a quiet part of the beach where they could change into their swimsuits without anyone seeing them, because eels are very shy,

and then he cried, "OK, off you go! You're free!
You're free!"

They all hugged and kissed him and promised
to send him postcards from America and Australia and then they rushed down the beach,
waving their buckets and spades, and jumped
into the sea with shrieks of joy.

"Eels!" exclaimed a huge shark, which happened to be passing at that moment. "My
favourite food!"

And in one gulp he swallowed the lot.

BRENDA SIVERS

Brenda Sivers was born in London. She studied languages at Southampton University and has since travelled widely – living and working in Zambia, Kenya, and Canada, where she worked in public relations and advertising, and for the Royal Bank of Canada, which gave her the opportunity to travel even more, from the Arctic Circle to Tijuana, the Caribbean and Europe! She now lives in Horsham, West Sussex, where she works for the Royal and Sun Alliance, writes novels when she can and plans to study for a zoology degree when she retires. She is married to a photographer, and has had nine children's books published so far, one of which won the Little Brown Canadian Children's Book Award.

A Cat Called
Conker

RACHEL ADAMS

Illustrated by
SAMI SWEETEN

For Mabel and for GEORGE with much love.

"How are you getting on at your new school?" asked Dad when I went to see him one weekend.

"Fine," I said, though it wasn't true.

"Made any friends yet?"

"Mm-m." This wasn't true either.

Luckily he didn't ask any more awkward questions and we went on our way to a butterfly garden. Dad always thought of interesting places for us to go together.

I'd tried telling Mum how I felt about the new school.

"It's so big and I don't know anyone!"

"Early days yet. You soon will. Your class teacher Mr Morris seems very nice."

"Ye-e-es. But when he says 'Take a partner' everyone except me has got someone to turn to.

And it's the same in the playground. I used to take conkers from our tree but now I haven't got any and when I try to watch the others they just tell me to push off."

Sometimes it's difficult to talk with grown-ups. You find yourself saying things just because you know that's what they want to hear. But when you try to tell them something you really want to say they don't listen properly and you know by their answers they haven't understood. Once I told Mum:

"Everything was fine when you and Dad and I lived in our house with a conker tree in the garden. Now you're in separate flats and I only see Dad at weekends and I've had to leave my old school where I had loads of friends!"

And all she said was:

"Getting used to change is part of growing up, love."

Grown-ups don't ask you when they're making plans, yet they expect you to go along with them. Wonder what they'd do if I said:

"I'm not going to school just for a change and because you're grown-up I expect you'll understand."

* * *

The flat Mum and I had moved into was on the second floor of a big block with a piece of fenced ground in front of it. One Saturday, when Dad was away working, Mum told me to go out and play there.

"I've got no one to play with!"

"Well, you must get some fresh air and I've no time to take you to the park. Don't go beyond the fence so I can keep an eye on you from the window."

As I stomped off down the cold stone steps she called after me,

"And watch out for dog doo!"

I hated those steps and thought of the warm wooden staircase at home.

The patch of ground was a miserable sort of place with rough grass and only a few trees. Nowhere to hide or build a den. I wandered round for a bit and was just going back in when I noticed something move in the branches of one of the trees.

I looked up and saw a small brown cat. Gran has a cat so I knew how to get its attention. I picked up a bit of stick and scratched the ground.

The cat began to take notice. I ended up in a circle I'd scratched round myself and the cat was down the tree in a flash. It put its nose on the ground and moved its head from side to side as its eyes followed the stick. Then it chased it, pouncing on it as if it was a mouse.

When Mum called from the window, "Lunch is ready!" the cat disappeared through a hole in the fence. By the time I'd squeezed after it I couldn't see the cat anywhere but what I did find were heaps of conkers, still in their prickly green cases, on the pavement in front of me. They'd fallen from a tree by a garden gate. I filled the pockets of my anorak, hurried home and told Mum I'd found them near the fence but I didn't say which side.

Next day for the first time I was keen to go to my new school. Swinging the conkers which Mum had helped me bake and string, I walked up to one group who were playing.

"Here, Chris! Let the new kid have a go with your ten-ner," someone said. Chris was one of those who'd told me to push off. I held out my biggest nervously as I watched Chris's swing

round and round before coming down on mine
hard. Splat! The group round us cheered and it
took me a minute to realize that the broken bits
on the ground were Chris's conker, not mine. As
we lined up to go in some of those near me
whispered,

"Great! That'll teach ole Big 'Ead!"

The cat was waiting for me when I went out to
play that evening. I wondered if it had a name.
Though it had no collar or name tag it didn't
look like a stray. Its silky fur was a different sort
of brown each time I looked and its eyes kept
changing colour too, sometimes blue, sometimes
grey.

"Well I'm going to call you Conker," I told it,
"because though you're soft and they're hard,
you showed me where they were."

School didn't seem so bad after that. In class we
were getting ready for a Hallowe'en party.

"Mr Morris says there'll be a prize for the best
costume from recycled materials," I told Mum.
She thought for a bit.

"I could make you a catsuit from old pairs of

tights. But you'd be a brown cat, not a black one."

Just like Conker, I thought and I gave her a hug saying, "I don't mind. Thanks, Mum!"

Mrs Patel who took the top class came to judge our costumes. At first we just walked round her but when Chris, who'd come as a fat orange pumpkin, began to wobble we started giggling. I decided to go round on all fours and when Mrs Patel handed me the prize – a book about the Rain Forest – I rubbed myself against her ankles. Everyone laughed and Chris fell into the tub of water with the apples. The party ended with most of us rolling around the wet floor laughing, surrounded by apples.

Mrs Beale, Chris's mother, who'd come to help Mr Morris with the food asked me to their bonfire party at half-term. So I had two Guy Fawkes' Nights because Dad took me to a Great Fireworks Spectacular at the football stadium. It was fantastic! The whole sky lit up with coloured stars which lasted for ages. The Beales' party was nothing like that but it was great fun. Chris

seemed a lot nicer at home. Together we made sure their dog Rikki was safe indoors with a bone and all the curtains were drawn so he wouldn't be frightened. We ate baked potatoes and gingerbread while Chris's father let off the fireworks just like Dad did for us last year.

Conker must have been somewhere safe too, for we played together every day that week. Whenever I looked up I saw old Mrs Giles knitting at the window of her flat on the ground floor. She always smiled and we waved to each other.

Soon after we went back to school Mr Morris told me Mrs Patel wanted to see me at break-time.

"My class are doing a pantomime," she said when I went. "It's *Dick Whittington* and as you seem to be able to behave exactly as a cat does I wonder if you'd play the part?"

I was very surprised but I heard myself saying, "Yes I'd love to." So nearly every lunch hour after that I went to her classroom to rehearse.

Just before the end of term we did a dress

rehearsal one afternoon for the school, and the next evening a performance for grown-ups. Mum came but Dad was away though he saw the video one of the teachers made. Everyone kept asking if I was nervous. It's strange but I wasn't. When I was with Dick it was just like playing with Conker except that on stage I was taking Conker's part. I did all the things I'd seen Conker do and tried to cheer Dick up as Conker had me.

Afterwards when Mum and I were going across the dark playground we overheard someone say:

"The child who played the cat must have watched cats for hours. Every movement was just right – made you realize how much you take them for granted. I'm going to get my Snowball a nice bit of fish tomorrow."

Must tell Conker, I thought, though we hadn't played together for a while since it was usually dark when I got home and Dad picked me up early on Saturdays. Mum squeezed my hand and whispered:

"She's right. You were splendid and I'm proud of you!"

When we got home she said:

"And now I've got some wonderful news to tell you!"

For one moment I thought she and Dad were getting back together again but she went on:

"Chris's mother has found us a flat with a garden! I'm going to move in while you're at your gran's over Christmas." She seemed disappointed that I didn't say anything.

"Aren't you pleased? Oh, poor lamb! You're probably over-tired from all the excitement. Bed now and in the morning I'll take you to see that flat as you're not going to your father's."

It was a really lovely flat with an overgrown garden that would be fun to explore. Yet all I could think about was Conker. When we got back I rushed outside. As I looked up at the bare branches I heard a rustling sound and saw something brown moving. It came gently down to the ground but it was only the last dry leaf blown by the wind.

"Something wrong?" I heard a voice say and there stood old Mrs Giles leaning heavily on her stick.

"I can't find the cat. You know. The one you've often seen me playing with."

"I've never seen any cat! Whenever I've seen you running and jumping you were always by yourself. Thought you were playing some sort of secret game."

I watched her go back slowly to the flats.

"I can see by the video you've settled down well in your new school," said Dad as we drove up to Gran's.

"Made lots of friends?"

"Yes," I replied and this time it was true.

RACHEL ADAMS

Rachel Adams was born in London and read History at Bristol University. She then taught in schools in Bristol for most of her career, and before retirement in 1992, was a head teacher. She still lives in Bristol, and enjoys gardening, meals with friends, and cats – especially her own cat, George! This is the very first children's story she has written.

She says: "Children's books have been part of my adult life for many years: reading to my class and, at one stage, reviewing for a local publication, Recent Children's Fiction. *They also formed a starting point for many of my school assemblies.*

"Between the acceptance of the adult world by infants and its challenging (and often rejection) by adolescents, is a brief period, roughly six to nine years, when a child is coming to terms with itself as an individual and with its relationship to the world outside the home. Books at this age can – in addition to their entertainment value – help it cope with this awakening process."

No Place Like
Home

JONATHAN WAKEHAM

Illustrated by
PHILIP HOPMAN

In memory of A.R.W., who started it all.

I.

On a great dark night
In the great dark city
The great dark house groaned.
Emily sat up, wide awake
And the great dark house groaned.

In the morning, munching breakfast,
Emily said,
"Did you hear the noise last night?"

"Which noise?" asked her father,
Tucked behind his paper.
"The noise like fifty crocodiles crying in the
    moonlight."
"No," said her father, "I heard nothing." And
    off he went to work.

The next dark night
In the great dark city
The great dark house roared.
Emily leapt up wide awake
And the great dark house roared.

In the morning, chomping cornflakes,
Emily said,
"Did you hear the noise last night?"
"Which noise?" said her father,
Hidden behind his paper.
"The noise like fifty lions fighting in the forest."
"No," said her father, "I heard nothing." And
    off he went to work.

The next dark night
In the great dark city
The great dark house shivered.

Emily jumped up wide awake
And the great dark house shivered.

In the morning, munching toast,
Emily said,
"Did you hear the noise last night?"
"Which noise?" said her father,
Hiding behind his paper.
"The noise like fifty dragons that forgot how to
    make fire."
"No," said her father, "I heard nothing." And
    off he went to work.

II.

Nobody knew
How many people lived in the great dark house.
"After all," said her father,
From behind his paper,
"They're not all like us you know."

So they kept the door
Extremely locked
In case the people not like them
Should come to call.

Emily's father worked in an office . . .
. . . somewhere . . .
in the great dark city,
Where he did . . .
. . . something . . .
All day long to pay the rent to pay to
Mr French,
Who owned the great dark house.

It was Mr French, said Emily's father,
Who kept his nose to the grindstone,
Took the shirt off his back,
Who worked him to the bone.

When Mr French came to call
The door was always, always open.

III.

And then,
On one great dark deep night,
The great dark house
Groaned
And roared
And shivered
All at once.

In the morning, chewing bacon,
Emily's father said,
"Did you hear the noise last night?"
"Which noise?" said Emily,
Acting innocent.
"The noise like a hundred crocodiles crying in
   the moonlight?"
"Yes," said Emily.
"The noise like a hundred lions fighting in the
   forest?"
"Yes," said Emily.
"The noise like a hundred dragons that forgot
   how to make fire?"
"Yes," said Emily.
"Hmm," said her father.
"I think it's time to call a plumber."

"To catch the crocodiles?"
"Yes," said her father.
"To calm the lions?"
"Yes," said her father.
"To teach the dragons to make fire?"
"Yes," said her father.
"And he might even help me with my grouting."

That day Emily did not go to school,
and her father did not go to work.
They spent the day together telephoning,
to try to find a plumber.
But when the plumbers heard
Of the great dark house
In the great dark city
They all said that they were too busy to help,
that they had no time for crocodiles
or lions
or dragons
or grouting.

At last, when a great dark night swallowed up
    the streets,
and a tired, smoky moon
Coughed
above the rooftops,
Emily began to cry.

And the great dark house began to moan,
Like a bear that has lost its hug
And they cried together in the moonlight,
Lost beneath the great dark sky.

IV.

Then, without a warning
(Like what? The stories never tell)
There was a knock at the door.

Stealthily
(Who knows what might be lurking there?)
Emily and her father unlocked the locks
Unchained the chains
Unbolted the bolts
And opened it

And saw an extra-
ordinary young man.

"My name is Peter," he announced,
"And I will be your plumber for this evening.
Apparently you have dragons."
Then he smiled a smile as warm as sunlight,
And said,
"Well, I guess we'd better take a look."

So they took the old and rusty grating
Off the heating
Leaving just a great dark hole and a far-off
   sound
Of swaying trees
And engines.

Then Peter climbed into the hole
With a torch between his teeth,
Smiled,
And disappeared into the dark.

Emily and her father waited.

Up and up and up and up
Past rivets and gratings and nuts and nails
Through pipes and valves and tunnels and tubes
And spider conversations
Scribbled in the dust
Peter climbed.

Higher and higher and higher and higher
Lost in the bricks of chimneys and walls
Tangled in wires and telephone lines
And spider cities
Strung across the rafters

STORY OF THE YEAR 4

Peter climbed.

And sat at last and listened
Listened to the great dark house.

Emily and her father waited.

V.

And suddenly there came a slither
Slither slither bump and slide
Peter falling sideways longways
Like a hare-brained fairground ride
Falling falling faster faster
There's no stopping
Till he . . .
"Ooooooooffff!"

"Hello," said Emily.
"Hello," said Peter.
"Can you fix it?" asked her father.
"Can you see which bolt to twist, which tap to
    turn?
And can you have a look at my grouting?"

But Peter said quite calmly,

"No.
The bolts are fine.
The taps are clean.
Everything is in perfect working order.
But your great dark house is crying,
And its heart is fit to break.
You never talk to the people next door.
You never ask if they are all right.
Nobody talks to anyone ever.
And your great dark house is lonely,
And its heart is fit to break.
You bolt your doors
And keep your eyes and ears
Extremely locked,
And your great dark house is home to no one,
And its heart is fit to break."

Her father said,
"It's not too late though?"
Emily said,
"To open the doors?"
Her father said,
"To give them cups of instant coffee?"
They both said,
"It's not too late though – is it?"

"No," said Peter with a smile as soft as sundown,
"It's not too late."
And he walked out softly, waving,
Into the great dark night.

VI.

The next day they began the transformation.
They unlocked the doors
Flung wide the dusty windows
And sluiced the rooms with cold bright tangy air
That you could taste right to your ankles.

Dancing badly to a marching tune
They broke the china pot beside the bookcase
And laughed, and munched on chips
With loads of ketchup
In bed, watching Gary Cooper.

That night her father made a cake
And they knocked on doors
All through the great dark house
And said, "We've made you cake and tea."
But no one came.

The next night he made chocolate biscuits
And they rang on bells
All through the great dark house
And said, "We've made you coffee and biscuits."
But no one came.

And then, one night
While Emily and her father
Sat up, reading stories,
A small shy dirty boy arrived
And asked if he could listen too.
"Of course," said Emily's father.

The next night
A small dark smiley girl arrived
And asked if she could listen too.
"Of course," said Emily's father.

And soon a little crowd of children
Tiptoed out along the passage
Past the grown-ups watching game shows
Past the fathers reading papers
To listen to the stories that he told.

And the great dark house seemed somehow
    lighter

And the moon smiled somehow sweetly
In the great dark sky above the city.

VII.

And then at last the grown-ups noticed
Wondered where their children were
Tore their eyes away from snooker
Trampled through the pizza boxes
Stamped along the passageway
To see just what was going on.

And the great dark house began to growl.

"Just what do you think you're doing?"
"Fill their heads with stupid stories!"
"There's no time for stupid stories!"
"What's the good of stupid stories?"

And the great dark house began to grumble.

"It's a great tough world out there."
"Everyone is out to get you."
"Mark my words – no time for stories."
"Has anyone called Mr French?"

And the great dark house began to tremble.

"I just wanted them to talk," said Emily's father.
"I just wanted them to know it's good
To know each other.
I never meant to . . .
Mr French!"

Mr French was on his mobile.
"Hello, ah yes, is that the police?
It's Mr French, I've caught a man;
We'll need your strongest prison van.
It's very sad – he works for me –
It's just the sort of thing I dread
But clearly he's been led astray;
He was once seen eating chips in bed.
Is he dangerous?
Well, yes.
He's telling stories it appears.
I'd suggest you lock him up
For at least a thousand years."

Then the great dark house began to shake
And roar
And rage beneath the city moon.
And suddenly
Quite silently

169

The fireplace reached out
And clamped its teeth
On Mr French's leg.

"Aaaaaaaarrrrrrrrrgggggggggghhhhhhhh!!!!!!!!"

And rugs rolled up and rolled up people
Taps tapped people on the head
Sofas swallowed up their sitters
Sleeping folk fell out of bed.

Pictures picked on people standing
Chairlegs kicked those sitting down
Mirrors flung back horrid faces
Doorframes frowned a fearsome frown.

"Quick!" cried Emily.
"See what you've done!
The great dark house is angry now."
And they began to run.

Pandemonium!
Down stairs
Down banisters
Down ladders hung from long-unopened dusty
   windows

Everybody fled
The great dark house.

But Mr French
– Unwisely, it appears –
Ran back,
To fetch his mobile phone
And was never
Ever
Seen again.

VIII.

And standing huddled in the street,
The people there began to talk
Of all that they had seen and heard
And passed round cups
Of instant coffee.

And in the morning,
When a single sooty bird began to sing
Above the rooftops
A little crowd of people stared
At a great light bright and smiling house
And realized that they liked each other.

And Emily's father,
With a smile as bright as sunrise,
Kissed her
And said, as if in perfect ending,
"Darling Emily, we're home."

JONATHAN WAKEHAM

Jonathan Wakeham was born in London, where he now lives. He read English at Bristol University, and now works for an advertising agency. When he was thirteen he was screen tested for Steven Spielberg's Empire of the Sun, *and has loved films ever since; he has written a screenplay,* The Return of Sleeping Beauty, *a sequel to the fairy tale. He has also written the lyrics for two musicals:* Paradise Lost, *premiered in Bristol in October 1995, and* The Capuccino Sea, *which opens next year.*

He says: "I've always told stories. I can't help it. Not all of them are any good; lots of them are terrible. It's normally my brother David, who is nine, who has to listen to them, and he tells me what's rubbish and what's good. A good story is like music; hundreds of people, even if they're very different, can enjoy the same story. That's really what 'No Place Like Home' is about. I hope it's a good one (David likes it), but I think you can do a better one. Don't you?"

The Girl Who Sold Slippers to Snakes

GHILLIAN POTTS

Illustrated by

GEORGIEN OVERWATER

To the memory of my mother, who always encouraged me.

L ong ago but not so long as all that nor so far that you could never reach it, there was a town where lived a woman with one daughter.

The daughter, who was called Stonecrop after the little plant which can flourish even on bare rock, was very clever. She was wise as well as clever; but her mother was not wise. Her mother was very proud of Stonecrop and unwisely she boasted of how clever her daughter was.

"She can cook as well as I can," boasted the mother. "She can sew with the tiniest stitches you ever saw. She can sing fit to charm the birds themselves and she can talk so well that she could persuade a snake to buy a pair of slippers!"

Now there were many other mothers in the

town who were quite as proud of their own daughters and they grew very tired of hearing how marvellous Stonecrop was. Perhaps if she had not been as pretty as she was clever they would not have been so jealous. As it was, three or four of them got together and decided to bring down the pride of Stonecrop's mother.

One said one thing, another said something else, they argued and even quarrelled a little but in the end they were all agreed.

They went to the young lord who was the town's protector and told him that Stonecrop was too clever to be allowed to live in that town.

"Why," they said, "her own mother says that she can sell slippers to snakes! Whoever heard of such a thing? She must be a witch!"

The young lord did not know that the women were jealous. He did not believe in witches. He just thought that Stonecrop must be very vain and boastful. So he said, "How does one tell a witch? Let her come to my Court of Justice and I will question her. I cannot send her away unjustly."

The women went away smiling. The first part of their plan was working. Now for the second part! They went to Stonecrop's mother and told her that the lord himself had heard of Stonecrop's cleverness and wanted to speak with her next day in the Justice Court.

"You must tell him about her," they said. "You know how modest she is. She will make no sort of a showing if you don't speak up for her. But don't say anything about it to her beforehand; she is so shy!"

Stonecrop's mother was so puffed up with pride that she suspected nothing. Next day, when the lord's officers came to tell Stonecrop that the lord wanted her to come to the Court, her mother ran ahead and as soon as the lord called for Stonecrop to come forward, her mother pushed in front and began to tell him how wonderful her daughter was, just as she always did.

"And she talks so well," she ended as usual, "that she could surely sell slippers to snakes!"

Stonecrop knew that she could not stop her mother boasting, so she had stood quietly waiting in the doorway until her mother finished.

The lord did not see her; he had grown impatient with her mother and now, angry, he exclaimed, "Then she had better go and do so! And never return to this town unless she can prove she has sold slippers to snakes!"

Then Stonecrop stepped forward and bowed to him and he looked and saw her for the first time and wished that he might take back the words he had just spoken. But spoken they were and nothing could alter them now.

However, that lord never afterwards gave any verdict, no matter how convincing the evidence, until after the accused had spoken. So some good came of it.

Stonecrop was hurt and angry at being banished in this way but she said nothing. She packed some clothes and food in a basket, said goodbye to her mother, who was weeping and wailing, and walked out of the city by the nearest gate. She had no idea where to go, so it did not matter which way she went.

She walked and she walked, and presently she came to a village. She asked if there were any snakes nearby.

"There's a mound where they lie in the sun sometimes," said the villagers. "We throw stones at them if we see them."

"Are they poisonous snakes, then?" asked Stonecrop.

"Don't know," said the villagers. "Who cares? A snake is a snake."

Stonecrop went to look. She saw lizards basking in the sun and then she saw the biggest grass snake she had ever seen.

Some of the village children had followed her. They began to throw stones at the snake.

"Leave it alone! It can't hurt you. Why kill a harmless snake?" asked Stonecrop.

"It's a snake!" yelled the boys. Stonecrop didn't bother to argue. She stood over the snake to shield it. The boys did not dare throw stones at her. They went away.

It was getting late. "I can't go to the village for shelter now," she said aloud to herself. "Where shall I go?"

As she stood gazing around her, the huge grass snake uncoiled itself.

Stonecrop started away from it in alarm. Then she remembered that it was only a grass snake and she stood still and watched it.

It reared up its head and seemed to inspect her, then turned and glided between the trees away from the road. Stonecrop hesitated for a moment, then followed it. The snake led her stealthily through the trees, across a small field and into a hollow filled with low bushes.

In the middle, so sunk into the ground and overgrown with mosses that it was almost invisible, was a tiny house.

The snake slid up to the door and drew itself slowly under it, into the house.

Stonecrop watched until its tail tip had vanished then went and knocked gently on the door. There was a faint scuffling sound from inside, then silence.

Stonecrop called out, "If you please! Your friendly snake led me here. Will you tell me where I may find shelter for the night?"

The door creaked open, just a crack, and someone peered at her. Then the door was opened wide and there stood a little old man, the smallest and ugliest Stonecrop had ever seen.

"If'n you bain't afraid of snakes," the old man said, in a voice as creaky as his door, "you c'n stay the night here."

Stonecrop thanked him. "I'm certainly not afraid of harmless snakes," she said. "But," she

added cautiously, "I am scared of poisonous ones."

The ugly old man grinned at her. "I ain't got no poisonous snakes," he told her. "Never worry, girl."

Even the grass snake seemed to have vanished. So Stonecrop spent the night quite peacefully. In the morning she told the old man her story.

"That is why I was willing to follow your snake," she explained. "I must find some way to make everyone think I have sold slippers to at least one snake, or never go home again. And what earthly use could a snake have for slippers?"

"No money for to pay for 'em, neither," said the little old man.

"It's hopeless," said Stonecrop sadly. "I haven't any slippers to sell, in any case!"

"Make some," said the old man.

Stonecrop thought and thought. Then she took long grasses and wove them together and shaped them into slippers.

"I have slippers," she said to the old man. "Now, how would a snake use them?"

The old man said, "Snakes like warmth."

Stonecrop thought some more. "Would your snake sleep in a slipper of grass?" she asked.

The old man nodded.

"Will you let me take your snake back to the town with me?"

"You saved him from the stones. He'll go with you," said the old man.

"But what about payment?" said Stonecrop. "I can't say I've sold the slipper if I haven't been paid!"

"Snakes go under the ground as well as on it," said the old man.

He went into the house. Presently the big grass snake came sliding out. It lowered its head and dropped something at Stonecrop's feet. When she picked it up, she found it was a ruby as large as her little fingernail.

"But this is far too much!" she said.

The snake glided towards the road. It seemed to beckon impatiently with its tail. So Stonecrop followed it. She called goodbye and thanks to the old man but he did not come out or answer.

"I'll come back and thank him properly later," she said to herself.

The snake led her to a short cut. When she was

sure of the way, Stonecrop carried it in her basket. It could not travel as fast and far as she could.

At last they came in sight of the town. Stonecrop let the snake coil around her shoulders. "You'll be safer there," she told it.

Everyone was very surprised to see her come back so soon and with a snake draped round her.

"Here is the snake I have sold a slipper to," Stonecrop told them, "and here is the payment."

When they saw the ruby, they ran to the lord's house to tell him. He came to meet Stonecrop and she told everyone how she had saved the snake and made it a slipper of grass. The snake coiled itself up in the slipper and everyone could see that it was pleased with it.

"Now," said Stonecrop, "I have done as you said and am no longer banished. But I will not stay here. I mean to go and live on my own, once I have taken this snake back to the old man."

And she refused to listen to anyone's persuasions. She gave the ruby to her mother and went on her way. Some of the townspeople tried to follow her, but the snake hissed at them so loudly that they were scared and ran back.

When Stonecrop got back to the hollow, the hut was gone. The little old ugly man was gone, too. Stonecrop was bewildered. She set the snake down in the grass.

"Can you find him?" she asked the snake. "I must thank him properly."

The snake reared up its head and looked at her. It seemed to want her to do something. Stonecrop stroked it gently and then looked away. When she looked back, the little old man stood there. The snake had gone.

"I do believe you're the snake!" cried Stonecrop, staring at him.

The old man grinned at her. "Took you long enough," he said.

Stonecrop flung her arms around him and kissed him. "Thank you," she began and then jumped back with a gasp. The little old man was growing and changing. He was taller than Stonecrop and young and good-looking. He was laughing with joy.

"Thank you, Stonecrop," he said. "You have broken both the spells that bound me. A wizard set them so that I must be a snake for half the time and an ugly old man the other half. Once someone knew the old man for the snake, I would be the old man all the time; and once a girl kissed me, ugly as I was, I would regain my real form. Will you marry me, Stonecrop?"

Stonecrop said, "I liked you when you were a snake and I liked you when you were an ugly little old man. I think I like you enough to marry you! But what shall we live on?"

"While I was a snake," said the young man, "I found many jewels. And as a little old man, I polished them. I think we shall have enough to live on."

So they were married and lived as happily and as long as was good for them.

GHILLIAN POTTS

Ghillian Potts was born in Surrey and now lives in Eltham, south-east London. She read English at King's College, London, and worked in publishing, bookselling, and finally teaching, which she loved, but resisted for many years because it was expected of her! She has four children and three grandchildren, and now works as a volunteer reader and editor for the Greenwich Talking Newspaper for the Visually Handicapped. *She enjoys bookbinding and embroidery (she makes rag books), woodworking and furniture restoration. She has had two pieces of children's literature published by Transworld – a narrative poem, and a story called* Sink or Swim.

She says: "I write for children because I started telling stories when I was about seven years old and never really grew out of it. I love telling stories and children are the best audience possible. Modern children's books do not talk down to children – an irritating feature of many children's books when I was a child – and I enjoy reading them. If I can write a story another child will enjoy reading, that is worth all the effort."

The children who helped judge this year's competition:

Ashleigh Arnott • Christopher Arnott • Mark Ayliffe • Claire Baker • James Baker • Sophie Bathe • Joe Beattie • Ashley Bendle • Robbie Blyth • Gregory Braney • Natalie Braney • Emily Bratt • Keely Buck • Tommy Burkin • Charlotte Burr • Louise Cartner • Mark Cheney • Jodie Clarke • Hanna Clarke • Sian Clarkson Cowles • Dora Coles • Lily Coles • Gemma Connor • Freddie Cox • Michael Crooke • Rosalind Cunningham • Christopher Daniels • Hannah Dinwiddie • Joe Dinwiddie • Katy Emms • Rachel Fisher • Louise French • Samuel Gamper • James Gansert • Michael Gibbs • Hayley Giles • Ella Gregory • Alicia Hagerty • Alexandra Hanlon • Gregory Harding • Robert Harland • Rebecca Harrington • Robin Heasman • Ian Henderson • Katie Henson • Anna Heppel • Jenny Heppel • William Hibberd • Edward Hill • Rosie Hill • Toni Holness • Christopher Homer • Bea Hooper • Sean Hughes • Ashley Humber • Meg James • Marie Kelly • Alice Kent • Verity King • Stacey Kingsman • Ben Kitchen • Grace Knights • Charlotte Lawrence • Laura Liddiard • Emily Little • Kelly Little • Hazel Luck • Elizabeth Ludlow • Richard Mallett • Jonathan Marshall • Christopher Martin • Katharine Martin • April Matthews • Hannah May • Kyle McGarey • Jamie McGregor • Lizzie McGregor • Jemma Mildon • William Milton • Amalia Morris • Claire Mould • Ben Mulford • Geoffrey Newnham-Smith • Lewis Newport • Rebecca Newport • Richard Nicholson • Marcus Nicholson • James Nobbs • Stephen Nobbs • Sophie Norris • Alistair O'Riordan • Clare Osborne • Nicola Oswald • Mark Paradine • Kinan Patel • Payal Patel • Taisha Patel • Vikki Perrett • Sammie Pickford • Annabel Pool • Natasha Prest-Smith • Adam Read • David Read • Gareth Reynolds • Lucy Rhodes • Paul Riri • Samantha Sharpe • Charlotte Smith • Holly Smith • Adam Sollis • Kyle Spence • Ginette Stewart • Daniel Stewart • Peter Stickler • Claire Sutton • Kate Tapper • Jackson Taylor • Simon Titcombe • Harriet Titmus • Richard Turner • James Walker • Katie Ward • Paul Wiggett • Marie Williamson • Claire Willis • Kerry Willis • James Willmott • Rebecca Woyensohn